AERIK'S
ANATOMY

AERIK'S ANATOMY

AERIK WILLIAMS
MD, MPH

ISBN Paperback: 978-0-578-63841-6
ISBN eBook: 978-0-578-63842-3

Printed in the United States of America

Cover and Interior Design: Ghislain Viau

To Max

May God bless and keep you always
May your wishes all come true
May you always do for others
And let others do for you

May you build a ladder to the stars
And climb on every rung
May you stay
Forever young

— Bob Dylan

Some **names** and identifying details **have been changed**
to protect the privacy of individuals.

Contents

Prelude

It's kind of random that I'm writing this book. I've never been a writer per se. I got As in high school English, but that's because the teachers liked me. As long as I smiled and was charming, I could obtain at least a B+. I struggled to read the assigned books, or at least the CliffsNotes, and had just enough understanding to get by. I was never much for thesis statements with supporting sentences grouped together succinctly in paragraphs. I found writing to be more of a chore or an exercise. There was a certain order to be followed, and disruption of the sequence would yield red arrows pulling sentences from one paragraph and inserting them into another. My English teacher would write lengthy notes in the margins, questioning why my topic sentence was unrelated to the supporting sentences. "This doesn't flow," she would write. "This is out of order." Perhaps my topic sentence didn't flow with my supporting sentences because I didn't want them to flow. Maybe I thought it read better out of order. Maybe I wasn't interested in structure.

I wasn't much on reading either. Aside from J. D. Salinger and a few John Irving novels, I only read if it was required. Most of my reading has not been for pleasure, but rather for academic survival. I've spent hours sifting out relevant details from physiology and immunology textbooks for the purposes of upcoming examinations, but rarely have I picked up a book for pleasure.

I've come to realize that I never enjoyed reading or writing because of my undiagnosed dyslexia. I get letters and words mixed up and it frustrates the hell out of me. Sometimes I even skip words. I read the same paragraph several times over just to make sure concepts are appropriately situated in my mind. For those who are adept, you would be amazed by the levels of misinterpretation of those with dyslexia. I often substitute words with identical first and last letters. Imagine reading the word "form" and substituting for the word "from," or reading the word "through" and substituting for the word "though." Adding or subtracting letters to words is not uncommon, i.e., reading "could" instead of "cold." I also substitute words that look similar, which changes the author's meaning. Sure, we are all subject to the occasional mishap, but imagine if it wasn't occasional. Imagine mishaps occurring with every sentence. It leads to reading and writing fatigue and an undesirable urge to put the book or the pen down.

I never had the intention of hiding my dyslexia. I thought struggling to get the right words out was normal. I mentioned it to my mother once while in elementary school, and she told me, "Ain't nothing wrong with you, boy." My mother was a schoolteacher, so I assumed she was correct. With that being said, I did notice that I was the student who was most limited by the allotted time for each examination. My verbal scores were good enough, but why was everyone finishing exams before me? I knew I had a problem my senior year of high school when reading Shakespeare aloud to the class. I didn't like Shakespeare and never had any idea as to what the hell he was talking about. I can't remember the character I was assigned, but I remember the struggle and I remember the embarrassment. I screwed up so many times that the teacher decided to reassign my character in front of the class. Damn, I can't read, I thought to myself. People were staring at me. Some students were smirking. I'm sure some were surprised.

I spent my college years avoiding classes that were heavy in reading and writing. I'd always known I wanted to be a doctor, so I stuck to the sciences. The courses with numbers and equations such as physics and calculus came easier. Classes in physiology and biology were mandatory for medical school applications and therefore could not be avoided. Though fascinating, I spent many hours tripping over my words. Did that say *aerobic, anaerobic,* or *anabolic*?

While in college, I noticed many students would read for fun. Harry Potter was popular, and my roommate finished the book in what seemed like one day. It would have taken me one month! One of my good friends, Dev, once asked me if I had read *The Alchemist.* "Hell no," I told her. "I don't like chemistry." I later learned the book has little to do with electron orbiting, but rather a shepherd and his journey to the pyramids of Egypt. She strongly recommended the book and so I attempted to read it. I thought it would be nice to have a book to talk about when other students on campus were discussing their most recent reads. Well, *The Alchemist* was awful. My mind wandered, the words skipped, and I had no idea what the author was talking about. My goodness, that book was boring. I made it through roughly thirty pages. I'm simply not sophisticated enough to read that "nonsense." That's what I call things that I don't understand—"convoluted nonsense." *The Alchemist,* of course, is not convoluted nonsense. It's only convoluted nonsense to me.

So how did I get here? For someone who despises reading and writing, I'm currently typing freely as thoughts race through my mind and are transported down to my fingertips.

When I was a senior in college, I took a course called The History of the American Automobile. It was a jock course. I was a soccer jock, so true to form, I decided to take Professor Stuart Leslie's class. It was easy! I read Lee Iacocca's autobiography and it was absolutely fascinating. I loved his grit. He was born to Italian immigrants. He made his way up the ranks at Ford Motor Company, and his leadership during Ford's economic volatile period was remarkable. Towards the end of book discussion, it dawned on me that I had never been this engaged with reading. I was actually looking forward to going to class. But was Lee Iacocca's story any more enthralling than *Great Expectations*, *The Adventures of Huckleberry Finn*, or *The Great Gatsby*?

The difference was not the book. The difference was the professor. His energy and enthusiasm were infectious, and that's all it took. I can't remember if he used a microphone in the Bloomberg Building at Johns Hopkins University, but he didn't need one. Instead of taking attendance, he gave us time cards that we would use to "clock in" to class. He spoke with order and structure in describing the evolution of the automobile; however, he allowed his students to think and write outside of these restrictions. My first assignment was simple: write about an automobile. That was it. There was no further instruction.

My father grew up in Youngstown, Ohio, as the youngest of three boys. His father worked at a steel mill and his mother worked at a department store folding boxes. The family of five didn't have much left over at the end of the month, but they had enough. My grandfather had to walk to work at times, but food was always on the table and a roof was over their heads. We would nowadays describe their house on Miltonia Avenue as meager. Zillow lists the sale price at just over $25,000. It's a single-family, two-bedroom home built in 1915, with just under 1,300 square feet of living space. The siding was originally yellow but morphed into an ugly beige color over the years. There was a small brick patio in the front and a parking shed in the back. My grandfather would sit on that patio and stare across the street while smoking a cigarette. He would be there for hours, just sitting and staring and smoking. Believe me, there wasn't much to look at. One side of the house was sectioned off by a chain-link fence that housed two loudly barking Dobermans. There was a gravel driveway and an uneven concrete sidewalk, an ankle sprain waiting to happen. There was nothing noteworthy on Miltonia Avenue, which makes the accomplishment of all three boys graduating from high school and college nothing short of miraculous.

My father went to medical school at THE Ohio State University. His admission story makes me laugh to this day. During his senior year of undergraduate study at Wilberforce University, he received a notice asking if he was interested in medical school. He checked the "yes" box and next thing you know, he was enrolled. Prior to checking this box, he had no idea what he was going to do after his senior year! This was the era of affirmative action. Understand that my father was more than competent. He excelled as an undergraduate student and as a medical student. He enjoyed a successful career as a primary care doctor in inner-city Columbus, Ohio.

Think about that concept. A student with the grades, integrity, and fortitude had no idea of his potential until someone asked him if he wanted to go to medical school. What the hell did he know about medical school? He grew up on Miltonia Avenue. Nobody on Miltonia Avenue ever went to medical school. How many other kids are stuck and will never maximize their potential because of limitations on their imagination? Trevor Noah describes this beautifully in his book *Born a Crime*, after a friend gives him the equipment necessary to burn music onto CDs and create an income that he never envisioned. Give a man a fish and you feed him for a day; teach a man to fish and you feed him for a lifetime. Just like Trevor, all my father needed was a fishing pole.

My father received his fishing pole and has been fed for a lifetime. This is personified not only in his medical career but also in the Columbus Metro Soccer Association, his own soccer league that he started from scratch in the mid-1980s. I had played soccer in the suburbs while in kindergarten and was the lone black kid on the team. I'm sure this was a bit odd for my dad, who grew up in a black neighborhood and played sports with black kids. So he observed the inner workings of the soccer league in the white suburbs and created his own league in the inner city. It wasn't difficult; it just took time and dedication. Prior to me kicking a soccer ball, he knew nothing of the sport and neither did any of the volunteer coaches. In fact, my Uncle Larry, who served as a coach, had his players doing some of his old football defensive lineman drills during practice. Football is all that he knew. In my father's short time as president of this league, he studied the sport and received advice from professional players and coaches in the area. Magic Celestin was a professional player from Haiti, and Lesh Shkreli was a professional player from Yugoslavia. He picked their brains and had these players perform clinics for us kids. He was steadfast and determined to make this league a success, and it was indeed a success.

He developed several players who would go on to play college soccer. I played at Johns Hopkins. My brother was the Ohio High School State Player of the Year. He led the Ivy League in scoring one season while playing at Yale. Pablo played at Harvard University. Elise played at Purdue University. Gavin and Rudy played at Bowling Green. Brett played at Otterbein University. Chad played at South Carolina–Spartanburg. Derek played at Brown University. Tim played at Guilford College. Ikenna played at Davidson College. Ptah played at UMass. Now that's impressive!

My father's most prized possession was my brother's soccer team. They were called the Zulus, named after the South African ethnic group known for their fearlessness and bravery. The Zulus took on my father's persona. They were strong and technical, with limitless imagination. They were warriors and they absolutely dominated.

My father's medical career brought financial success and he couldn't wait to purchase his first luxury car. Who could blame him, having grown up on Miltonia Avenue? He came home from the Ed Potter Mercedes-Benz dealership on Fifth Avenue one afternoon, rolling in an orange diesel Mercedes-Benz. It was slick! The color was obnoxious. The headlights were yellow and white and they sat in a chrome grille. A silver Mercedes-Benz ornament was fixed to the hood. At the time we lived in a middle-class neighborhood and our neighbors were less impressed with the car than we were. They actually booed when he pulled it into the driveway. "Just jealous," my mother would say. My father didn't care. He was a Zulu and Zulus don't give a damn. He would later admit that it wasn't a wise purchase, but when you grow up on Miltonia Avenue, you think fancy things aren't meant for people like you. To be more specific, when you grow up on Miltonia Avenue, you are certain that a Mercedes-Benz is not for people of color unless you're an icon. There were no icons on Miltonia Avenue. A poor kid wanted to treat himself, and there was nothing wrong with that.

That orange Mercedes-Benz provided me with material for a paper assigned by Dr. Stuart Leslie nearly eighteen years after its purchase. The Mercedes-Benz logged thousands of miles and it gave me many firsts. I wrote freely about that car. I documented the time my sister ate my mother's chocolate bar while sitting in the back seat. She lied and blamed it on me, despite the chocolate that was smeared across her face. My mother told her that she was going to the devil for lying. I recounted the time my mother left her three children in the car while she went into a shoe store. "Don't touch anything," she told us. "I'll be right back." Leaving kids in the car for fifteen minutes, regardless of the temperature, was not an uncommon practice in the 1980s, or at least it wasn't in the Williams household. In her absence, my younger brother put the car into neutral and we drifted backwards down a decline.

We fortunately hit a parked car at a slow enough speed to spare any damage to the Mercedes or our little body parts! I was also in the back seat while parked at the post office when an old white man yelled at my mother, "Where did a nigger like you get a car like that?" My mother jumped out of the front seat and she cussed at him. That was the first time I had ever been called a nigger. This was also the first time I saw the fight ingrained in my mother, a manifestation of her upbringing in inner-city Newark, New Jersey.

I was congregating with students at a small group session outside of Bloomberg Hall when Dr. Leslie approached me. "That paper you wrote was spectacular." I didn't think he was talking to me. Certainly, he had the wrong student. I had never been congratulated on writing anything. He extended his hand towards me. "What are you going to do after graduation?"

"Well, I'd like to go to medical school," I said. I shook his hand, now certain that he was addressing me.

"You may be missing your calling. If you ever decide to write anything, I would like to read it. If you ever need help with anything, let me know." Dr. Leslie sent the paper to the editors at the *Johns Hopkins Magazine* and they agreed with his assessment. I became one of only a few students to have their work published in the magazine.

Just like my father, I had a talent, but it wasn't recognized until someone made me aware. I spent my entire academic career writing in a box. The consequence for deviation was a red pen with notes scribbled in the margin, until I met Dr. Leslie. I haven't written for enjoyment since I wrote about the orange Mercedes. I've scribbled equations on note cards, documented patient histories and physical examinations, and written my own notes in the margins of pathology textbooks. This, however, was obligatory. My desire to write freely has been perpetual since the afternoon Dr. Leslie complimented my work.

So here I am, preparing this book. I have channeled the resolute Zulu spirit and allowed my imagination to guide me. Take my hand and walk with me through my journey in medicine. Follow me through *Aerik's Anatomy*.

CHAPTER 1

Death

I would like to dedicate this chapter to Dr. Kilmer. Before I go into details on how experiencing death in the hospital has altered my life, please allow me to share his story.

Dr. Kilmer

The first two years of medical school at THE Ohio State University were a blur. My schedule was predictable. Every three weeks we had a comprehensive examination that required hours of preparation. I was up at 7:00 a.m. to grab a quick breakfast. Class started at 8:00 a.m. and lasted until early afternoon. I ate lunch after class and then hit the library for a few hours. In the evening, I would leave the library and head to the gymnasium for weight lifting and basketball, then back to the library for late-night studying. As the exam date approached, I spent less time at the gymnasium and more time in the books. This routine required diligence. I would memorize hundreds of pages of material over three weeks and regurgitate the information during the exam. Missing one day of study would reflect on my exam score, particularly considering my dyslexia. Our exam motto was "65 to stay alive," a reflection of the minimum 65 percent passing score. Three failed exams meant an unsavory meeting with the academic board and repeating the academic year. To add insult to injury, repeating the year also meant another year of tuition, which equated to $30,000.

Exams were pressure packed. My buddy D Mos had a history of irritable bowel disease, which to the annoyance of anyone in his vicinity, would flare under the pressure of the examination. I too was not immune to test anxiety. I spent the first ten minutes of the exam just settling myself down. I would close my eyes and take deep breaths. I wouldn't look at the first question until I could no longer feel my heart beating through my shirt. As the exam progressed, my nerves would settle. I would put a check mark next to the questions in which I wasn't sure of the answer. Once I completed the exam, I would review all of the check marks, and as long as I was sure of 65 percent of my answers, I knew I was safe.

The weekend following the exam was our opportunity to let loose. Three weeks of pressure-packed studying culminated with a weekend of booze, football, and hip-hop clubs. High Street on campus provided us with plenty of opportunity.

We frequented fine establishments, such as the Buckeye Nut House, which seemed to pay no attention to drinking age requirements. We would roll about ten deep into the club. We donned our medical school T-shirts, which would increase the opportunity to meet a young lady. We drank enough alcohol and danced enough in one weekend to hold us over for the next three weeks.

The Sunday after the exam was for recovery. I would hydrate myself with Gatorade in the morning and eat one of my mother's bacon, egg, and cheese English muffins. I would hit the gymnasium at noon and come home for my only nap for the next three weeks. I would wake up in time for dinner and late-night television. Monday morning, I was up at 7:00 a.m., back to the routine.

At the start of my second year, I noticed a few of my classmates were walking in and out of the first-year lecture hall. "D Mos, what's up with Q?"

"Q didn't pass, man. Sixty-five to stay alive." I didn't know what to say. I felt for Q. I couldn't imagine repeating the entire academic year. I couldn't imagine the embarrassment of seeing your former classmates.

Q wasn't the only one. Medical school is difficult and it's not for everyone. Even some diligent students aren't able to keep up. With that being said, some failing students only had themselves to blame. It turns out that a few students partook in extracurricular activities every weekend, and not just following exams. Matter of fact, some students partook in daily activities conducive to failing medical school. That's a lot of money and time to throw away.

Our first two years of study laid the foundation of our medical knowledge. Just as important, they prepared us for our first licensing examination. A high licensing exam score puts students in a position where they are competitive for the more selective residency programs. Medical schools are also judged on the percentage of students that pass the licensing examination. To ensure students progress through the first two years of medical school and perform competitively on the licensing exams, schools often hire faculty to teach board review.

Our board review faculty consisted of one man, Dr. Kilmer. I actually met Dr. Kilmer many years prior while I was in high school. I sat next to his son in the jazz band. He was very eccentric and resembled "Doc" from *Back to the Future*. He had a few strands of silver hair that were always impeccably slicked back. Despite his protruding stomach, he walked with purpose and at a brisk pace, and he never really made eye contact with you while he was talking. He would roll his eyes to the back of his head and flicker his lids. He talked with a bit of a lisp. His tone was sporadic, oscillating from high pitch to low pitch and high decibel to low decibel within the same sentence. He seemed to always speak about medicine in hyperbole and with a high degree of passion. It was as if he was in a relationship with medicine. He was particularly fond of the heart. He would stop mid-sentence during a lecture and stare at the projector screen to admire its cardiac vessels and striated muscles. He spoke passionately about Starling's forces, the strength of the heart's systolic contraction. He was in love with medicine. He was also in love with educating students. But most importantly, he was in love with THE Ohio State University College of Medicine. Dr. Kilmer was legendary. In fact, he was on staff when my father was in medical school at Ohio State many decades prior. If anybody wanted a fight with hundreds of medical students, say something bad about Dr. Kilmer.

His office was in the basement of the lecture hall. He kept the overhead lights off at all times and relied solely on his desk lamp. If you walked by his office, you might catch a glimpse of his silhouette, or that of his cat. On occasion, I was in the lecture hall many hours past midnight, cramming for an exam. I would walk by his office and his light would still be on. Did he ever sleep? He was a peculiar man, but that's what the medical students loved about him.

We failed Dr. Kilmer. Whether it was the late-night partying, lack of study, or lack of determination, I really don't know, but we failed him. Nearly 10 percent of the class didn't pass the medical licensing examination after the second year of medical school. Dr. Kilmer took it pretty hard, but he's the type that turns frustration into determination. He ratcheted up the review course. There was mandatory study hall with Dr. Kilmer for those who failed. He became even more eccentric, more passionate, and more peculiar. Students were determined to not let him down again.

Despite his efforts, the powers that be removed Dr. Kilmer from his position. We all were in shock. We threatened to revolt, but we had no leverage. I had a friend that was in the basement of the lecture hall when the maintenance crew carried his desk out of his dimly lit office. Dr. Kilmer stood outside and watched them walking down the hall, uncontrollably weeping. He was despondent and overcome with grief.

Graduation from medical school is long awaited. I felt as if I was on top of the world. My parents were so proud and I was proud of myself. One of the best gifts that I've ever given my father was on graduation day. Medical students are ordained by having a garb called a hood placed over their shoulders and fastened around their neck in front of the audience. As storied tradition has it, those placing the hood must be physicians themselves. My father, class of 1978, would be hooding me, class of 2008. For those without physicians as family members, they often chose faculty members for the proceedings. Dr. Kilmer hooded a countless number of students that day, an immeasurable showing of gratitude and appreciation. I noticed there was something off, however. He wasn't cheerful. He seemed to be depressed. I smiled at him following the ceremony, and he only nodded back. His lack of emotion saddened me and gave me a very uneasy feeling.

I was at the pool only a few days later when I got the message. Dr. Kilmer had killed himself. It makes me uncomfortable to this day. A man who loved his job and students so much that he couldn't bear life without them. This felt different than all other death I experienced during medical school. This was personal. You are loved and you are missed, sir. Rest in peace.

Prelude to Death

In 1952, Mother Teresa opened Kalighat Home for the Dying in Kolkata. This converted Hindu temple serves as a refuge for the poor facing imminent death. According to one volunteer, "Many people have such frail stick like bodies, and many contorted and amputated. I was afraid bones might snap as I helped one woman get up from her bed and try to walk to a chair for lunch."[1] Similar to hospice, patients receive medical care if necessary, but the focus is on comfort care. Mother Teresa believed in the opportunity for everyone to die with dignity. The Kalighat Home is for all of God's children. Muslims are read the Quran before death and Catholics are read their last rites. There is no room for divisiveness. "A beautiful death," she said, "is for people who lived like animals to die like angels—loved and wanted."[2] I've seen my share of death, but I'm not Mother Teresa. I had no firm ground to stand on.

One of my favorite books, *Crash the Chatterbox*, written by Steven Furtick, mirrors this message. As an aside, I have found that listening to audiobooks makes "reading" more tolerable. Steven Furtick is the pastor of Elevation Church. The church is based in Charlotte, North Carolina; however, there are Elevation campuses spread from Toronto to Melbourne, Florida. He's not your traditional pastor. He wears skinny jeans and "smedium" sized T-shirts to accentuate his burly muscles. His Jordan shoe game is on point. He epitomizes the era of the young and hip pastor. His message is about love and is centered on the true meaning of the gospel. The word of God is never intended to make one feel inferior, unworthy, or unwanted. The word is to inspire! Pastor Furtick does inspire by reminding that all fall short of the glory of God, but through grace we move forward. It's a "me too" church. "You yelled at your kids this week? Me too!" he exclaims. "You mean you have doubts about some of the things you read in the Bible? Me too! ... You lose your temper? Me too! ... You wanted to cuss somebody out this week in traffic ... Me too! If Paul struggled, you'll struggle; if Paul suffered, you'll suffer."

In a passage in his book, Pastor Furtick sets the scene by describing his son's T-ball league. It's a league in which there are no rules. For all parents who have children that play T-ball, I'm sure you can relate. Kids can run clockwise around the bases without penalty, "outs" aren't always called "outs," the kids don't necessarily play their positions, and most importantly, nobody is keeping score. Most parents aren't bothered by the lack of structure. This isn't the World Series, after all. They are happy that for at least an hour little Suzie won't be complaining about who ate her peanut butter cookie and little Cameron won't be playing on the iPad. It's an opportunity to exhale while someone else is responsible for your child's well-being. It's also comical to watch them trip over the bases and dance the "floss" while bored in the outfield.

Pastor Furtick and his son, however, are of a different ilk. They need structure. They need to know the score. An "out" is an "out." There is a winner and a loser. You can imagine the difficulty they experienced in the chaos that is little league T-ball. Instead of the natural response of frustration, he and his son created their own set of rules, paying no attention to the chaos on the bases or in the outfield. They would play the game the correct way. Once his son made a play in the infield or made contact with his bat, he would look towards his father. Steven Furtick would give his son a thumbs-up, indicating success. So when his son was lost in the world of chaos, he decided not to partake in the chaos, but rather seek guidance from his father. He didn't allow himself to be subject to lawlessness, because the end result is disorder. He wasn't concerned about how the umpire was calling the game. He wasn't concerned that Suzie was running the wrong direction. He wasn't concerned that Cameron batted out of order. He was even unaware that Jacob was "dabbing" in the dugout. He had detailed instructions that were given to him by his father, and he looked only towards him for approval.

I love this metaphoric passage in Pastor Furtick's book. No matter the chaos in your life, if you are grounded in what it is you believe, you don't have to become subject to the surrounding dysfunction. Well, like I said, I'm not Mother Teresa and my last name is not Furtick.

Dorothy

Entry onto the medical wards as a third-year student is met with excitement by many; however, it was downright frightening for me. I fear the unknown and I fear looking stupid. There are hundreds of cancer types, skin diseases, endocrine diseases, eye diseases, intestinal disorders, infectious diseases, etc. How was I going to piece it all together? No board exam or standardized patient can prepare you for the medical wards. I was up fairly late before my first day as a third-year student, trembling with fear. My stomach tossed and turned and I was overwhelmed with anxiety. In the wee hours of the morning, I grabbed one of my textbooks and began reviewing, but there was so much information and I didn't know where to start. Should I review treatment for community acquired pneumonia, the risk factors for developing heart disease, cancer screening recommendations, the signs of end organ damage in hypertensive emergency? I felt sick. My bulldog Willa could sense my anxiety. She nestled her fat body against my legs. I petted her back with long strokes, which caused her to wiggle. I envied her stress-free life. No expectations for Willa. Before long, we both fell asleep.

My first rotation was on the Internal Medicine service, and fortunately I was paired up with my buddy Tone. Do you remember the character Stifler in the movie *American Pie*? Well, that's Tone. He had an obsession for attractive women, threw legendary medical school parties, and didn't let anything get under his skin. The guy was always cool and unfettered, just what I needed to calm my nerves. Unfortunately, our attending physician was a hard-ass. She was in charge and made sure that everyone knew it. She had an imposing figure and always wore a quizzical look, as if she were dissecting you. She was very self-righteous and at times nonsensical. I still remember my first day on service, discussing a patient who had just arrived to the Medicine floor from the emergency department. "Patient is a forty-five-year-old female with a past medical history of—"

"Stop!" she interrupted. Her voice sent a jolt through my body. I jumped with fear. "What do you mean by female? Females can be dogs! Is she a dog?" I wanted to ask her if she had ever seen a dog lying in a hospital bed. What kind of dumb question was that? I could tell she would be riding my ass throughout the rotation. I glanced over at Tone. He had his arm extended with his palm facing downwards. It was his hand gesture telling me to chill out.

"She's a forty-five-year-old woman!" the attending exclaimed.

I couldn't help but roll my eyes. "Did you just roll your eyes at me?" the attending snapped.

I didn't respond, not wanting to buck the system on my first day. Whatever, I thought to myself. What does any of this have to do with her pneumonia? That afternoon, Tone pulled up a chair next to mine at the nursing station. "Dartos, it's the first day! You need to chill out," he said.

We all had nicknames in medical school. My buddy Mark was called "Napster" because he could hook your computer up with mp3s. Saeed was from California, so we called him West-Saeed. One girl would interrupt the professor all the time, so we called her "Excuse me, professor." My nickname in medical school was "Dartos." In medical terminology, dartos is defined as a layer of connective tissue found in the penile shaft, foreskin, and scrotum.

As I was saying … "Dartos, you need to chill out," Tone said. "She rides me too. It's how she gets off. Don't let her bother you. Just answer her questions and it will all be over in two weeks."

"Well, I'm not kissing her ass," I told Tone. He just nodded his head and gave me a wry smile. I knew that wry smile. It meant he was up to something. The last time I saw that wry smile he was convincing a girl at a bar on High Street that he was a plastic surgeon. He also convinced her friend that I was a neurosurgeon, and she bought it.

Her friend approached me and said, "I know that you can't talk long because you're on neurosurgery call, but your friend Eduardo said you would like some company." I looked over at Tone and he had that same wry smile on his face. He was always changing his name when talking to women. One evening he was Rodrigo, the next evening he was Sebastian. If the conversation was boring and he lost interest, then he would use the name Dwight Mosley, which was the real name of one of our classmates. He lifted his beer in the air from across the bar, as if to say "Cheers." It's a good thing she didn't ask me anything about neurosurgery.

I looked over at Tone's computer screen. He was searching the attending's pager number. "She's right behind us. You don't have to page her," I told him.

"I know what I'm doing, Dartizzy," he said, still smiling. He typed her pager number into the screen, and a picture of her appeared. He then typed an unfamiliar number into the "Return Page Number" box. "What number is that?" I asked him.

"It's the number to the Columbus Gay Men's Choir," he chuckled. Holy shit! Convincing a girl you are a plastic surgeon named Eduardo is one thing, but paging the attending physician to the Columbus Gay Men's Choir is crossing the line. That will get you kicked out of medical school! He very calmly rose from his seat and left the medical floor. Before I could grasp the depths of his shenanigans, the attending's pager started going off. I couldn't get up and leave. That would look suspicious, so I just sat there. I could feel her presence behind me.

"Excuse me, Aerik, I need to call this number back," she said as she reached for the phone. Well, I certainly couldn't get up now. I watched her dial the number. It felt like an eternity before someone answered.

"This is the Columbus Gay Men's Choir," a cheery voice answered. The attending slammed the phone down.

My internal medicine clerkship will always be remembered for the Columbus Gay Men's Choir and for Dorothy. Dorothy was a very sweet ninety-three-year-old lady whose joy for life was undeterred despite losing her husband only a few years earlier. She lived in a local nursing home, and per the staff, she was very sharp without any evidence of slowing down. She enjoyed singing and was a regular at music activities. She also enjoyed knitting during arts and crafts hour. She was very witty, making the nursing home staff chuckle with her humor. Dorothy was healthy and had no past medical history. She had shown no signs of dementia and was very independent. Therefore, alarm bells sounded one afternoon when she began muttering incoherent phrases and gesturing towards items on her wall. The nursing home staff called EMS and she was sent to the Emergency Department. She was accompanied by her niece, who rushed over to the hospital the second she was alerted that her aunt was acting strange. "She wasn't acting like this last week," said Dorothy's niece.

The ER staff checked routine labs and ordered a CT scan of her head. One must consider central nervous system disease in elderly patients with acute change in mental status. A CT scan of the head in these clinical scenarios can be useful. Dorothy's CT scan was normal; however, she did have a lab abnormality. The sodium level in her blood was significantly reduced, a condition referred to as hyponatremia. Low sodium levels can cause a change in mental status, and when levels are significantly reduced, patients can develop seizure activity. In the elderly, dehydration is a common cause of a hyponatremic state. Very simply, Dorothy hadn't been eating or drinking much during the high summer temperatures and she became so dehydrated that her sodium levels fell to dangerous levels. Fortunately, all Dorothy required was some intravenous saline solution, administered over the course of a few days.

I presented Dorothy's case to my attending, and after she asked me a few irrelevant questions, we put in nursing orders to replace Dorothy's sodium. Replacement was slow and steady, careful not to correct her blood sodium levels too quickly, which could also result in seizure activity. Over the next two days I followed Dorothy's progress. I checked several sodium levels and titrated the rate of the saline solution. I took pride in her care. I relished the responsibility. I don't think I could have given my own mother better care. After a couple of days, Dorothy became cognizant of her surroundings. I found her to be as witty as described. "I have to get out of here! No bingo in the hospital," she would tell me. It wasn't that simple. We couldn't just discharge her. She was an elderly woman and two days of lying in a hospital bed zapped all of her energy. I consulted the physical therapy team and asked them to get her back up to speed before we sent her home.

"Just a couple more days, Dorothy." She rolled her eyes. The physical therapist brought Dorothy into the hallway of the medical ward. With deliberate and unsteady steps on her walker, Dorothy made her way. She was determined, and so very cute. The staff marveled at her progress. She smiled when she passed by the nursing station. "No bingo in the hospital, Aerik," she repeated herself. I knew I was going to miss her.

A new attending took over the medicine service just before Dorothy's discharge. "Thank goodness," I said to Tone. The new attending was the polar opposite of the previous one. He pushed the medical students to perform, but in a nonmalignant fashion. He had high expectations but was devoid of the attitude. He prioritized education and quality care. He also had a sense of humor, which was in tune with his Peter Griffin appearance.

The new attending and I saw a patient who had recently been transferred to the Internal Medicine service. He had presented with fevers, atypical infections, and a rash over the past few months. He had flesh-colored bumps on his legs, arms, and chest. The ER physicians ran a Human Immuno-deficiency Virus (HIV) PCR blood test, which had come back positive. The patient was unaware of the lab result and we would have to break the bad news. The attending introduced himself and shook the patient's hand. "How long have you had that rash?"

"The past few months," the patient said. "It seems to be getting worse."

"What does that look like to you?" the attending asked me.

The question caught me off guard. I knew the answer. The rash was molluscum contagiosum. What I couldn't figure out was why he was asking the question in front of the patient. In medical school, students are frequently asked questions in front of patients. It may cause students to sweat, but it's educational. In my current role, I ask students questions about a disease state in front of a patient all the time; however, in the case of a man with newly diagnosed HIV, it didn't seem to be appropriate.

If I were to ask a medical student what causes eczema to flare in front of a mother who brings in her child for eczema management, it's not a big deal. It's just eczema. I'm testing the medical student's knowledge base. Eczema can be a nuisance, but it's treatable and typically has minimal impact on the patient's life. If I were to ask a medical student the difference between small cell and non-small cell lung cancer in front of a patient that has just been diagnosed with lung cancer, this would not be appropriate. What's the difference? Wouldn't I just be testing the medical student's knowledge base?

The answer lies in our value of humanity. A range of emotions should be expected in the patient with newly diagnosed lung cancer. There may be fear, anxiety, sadness, anger, etc. To talk about the disease state flippantly, while the patient is experiencing this range of emotions, prioritizes the disease over the patient. Instead of being identified as Fred with newly diagnosed lung cancer, the patient is identified as non-small cell lung cancer in a person who's name just so happens to be Fred. It's dehumanizing. To flippantly ask me about a rash in front of a newly diagnosed HIV patient, while they are traveling through the range of emotions described above, is inconsiderate. I wanted the patient to know that I saw him as a human being first, and not as a viral infection. I decided not to answer the question. I felt as if my answer could wait.

"Sir, I've got some news about the blood tests that were run in the Emergency Department," said my attending. "I'm sorry to tell you this, but your HIV test came back positive." I felt a sickening feeling in the pit of my stomach. Can you imagine a physician giving you such life-altering news? This was 2006 and the HIV population was unfortunately siloed and shunned by segments of society. Certainly the same is true today, but to a lesser extent. How would he divulge this news to his loved ones? Would he still be accepted?

To my surprise, the patient wasn't bothered. "I knew you were going to say that," he said as if I had just diagnosed him with hypertension. "Just put me on the medicine."

"That's it? No other questions?" my attending asked.

"How long do I have to stay here?" asked the patient. One thing I learned about patients in the hospital is that they are always ready to leave.

"I guess he's got stuff to do," my attending said jokingly after we left the patient room. "Oftentimes they know, Aerik. They know the risk factors and they know the symptoms. Many times they know others with the disease." The attending could tell that I was a bit rattled.

"Molluscum contagiosum," I said.

"Excuse me?" said the attending.

"The rash, sir. It was molluscum."

"You got it!" said the attending while giving me an exuberant slap on the back.

I was finishing the history and physical notes in the patient's chart when the overhead system was activated. "Rapid Response. Room 310." A caravan of nurses and doctors rushed past me. The Rapid Response Team is called at the early signs of a patient's clinical deterioration in order to prevent cardiac or respiratory arrest. These patients are typically high acuity and need immediate intervention. Medical management with intravenous fluids or antibiotics may be necessary. Consultation of specialty services may be in order. Some of these patients may need to be transferred to the critical care units for more intensive medical intervention. Medical students weren't assigned to the Rapid Response Team, but I was eager to gain as much experience as possible. I followed the rush of doctors and nurses to Room 310 when it hit me. That's Dorothy's room!

By the time I made it to her room, the response team had already started triage. They were reading my most recent note aloud. "She is a ninety-three-year-old female who presented two days ago with changes in mental status secondary to hyponatremia. Serum sodium has been corrected. She worked with physical therapy this morning in anticipation of discharge. What was her serum sodium this morning?" the senior resident asked.

"One thirty-three," I answered confidently. I stared at Dorothy. She looked exactly the same as a few hours prior. She had the same pink color in her face. She had a pulse and she was breathing on her own. The only difference was that she was nonresponsive. She wasn't gesturing towards items on the wall. There was no insensible speech. She was alive, but she was just there. It was as if her body was empty. The resident balled his hand into a fist and sternly rubbed her chest. She didn't budge. He pried open her eyelids.

"Her pupils are dilated. Send her to radiology for a head CT stat!"

"What the hell is going on?" I said to myself. She was just walking up and down the medical ward on a walker an hour ago. Did I miss something?

Tone tapped me on the shoulder. "What's up? Was that Dorothy on the stretcher?"

"Yup. I don't know what the hell happened. She wanted to play bingo just a few hours ago. Now she's comatose. Chief said her pupils are dilated."

"Maybe she had a stroke," he said. I shrugged. Tears welled up in my eyes.

My mind wandered over the next thirty minutes. I realized I had yet to eat lunch. Funny how I didn't feel hungry. I was getting used to the Medicine floors. Hours of rounding on patients, giving them the best of myself. It was a trade-off. I've learned that we often trade our health and comfort for that of the patient. You don't realize it until you've lost or gained weight. You don't realize it until you're yelling at your spouse. You don't realize it until you've missed your child's dance recital. The expectation is that you always give of yourself, even at the risk of your own health.

We received a phone call from the radiologist as Dorothy was being transported back to her room. She had suffered a hemorrhagic stroke. The radiologists had reviewed the CT scan with the neurosurgery team, and it was decided that Dorothy was not a candidate for surgical intervention. Dorothy was actively dying. Her niece had arrived at the hospital and we delivered the bad news. She began sobbing amongst the clinical staff. Dorothy's blood pressure increased to dangerous levels and her heart rate began to slow. Cushing reflex, I thought to myself. It wouldn't be long. Within fifteen minutes, a nurse alerted a senior resident that Dorothy was no longer breathing. In that moment, Dr. Tinu, the intern on the Medicine service, turned to Dorothy's niece and offered the most thoughtful gesture that I have seen in my years as a doctor. He asked her if she would like to hold Dorothy's hand. How comforting. A familiar touch as she departed this world and entered the heavenly kingdom. "A beautiful death is for people who lived like animals to die like angels—loved and wanted."

I was unprepared for Dorothy's death, but I was also unprepared for what transpired next. Everyone went back to work! It wasn't callous. After all, there were several dozen patients on the medicine ward that needed our attention. I went back into her room about an hour after her death and her body had already been taken to the morgue. That was it. No more Dorothy. Before long, the ER called my senior resident. We had another patient to admit to the Medicine floors.

Crossroads

A few months after Dorothy's passing, I had seen more death and morbidity than I had ever cared to. I became hardened and insensitive. My emotions following Dorothy's death were fleeting. A young man my age was admitted to the hospital after a gunshot wound left him paralyzed. I took his history and presented his case to my attending, unmoved by his terminal paraplegic state. Not my fault. Shouldn't have been gangbanging. You play with fire, you get burned. Time to go back to work.

I wasn't alone in this thinking. Internal Medicine residency is absolutely exhausting. The hours are long and the medical cases can be very complicated. Rarely is only one organ system involved. The patient comes into the hospital with pneumonia and low blood pressure. You treat the pneumonia with antibiotics and the low blood pressure with intravenous fluids. Oops, you gave too much fluid. Now the patient's heart failure is active because of fluid overload, and their kidney function is now impaired because of the heart's reduced ability to pump. Tweaking the management of one organ system has profound effect on another.

Due to the complexity of patient management, the Accreditation Council for Graduate Medical Education (ACGME) limits the number of patients a resident can admit to the hospital on any given day. This limitation also helps to prevent physician fatigue and subsequent error. You certainly wouldn't want a drowsy doctor with brain fatigue typing in your medical orders or performing a lumbar puncture.

One evening I was discussing the stress involved in patient care with a senior resident. I told her that I had become immune to death. "It doesn't get any better," she said. "I remember once being on call with my senior resident. We got slammed! We were one admission from our daily limit when the Emergency Department called at 4:00 a.m. We were exhausted. We'd arrived at the hospital at the butt crack of dawn. The only food we'd had all day were the Little Debbie snacks we carried in our white coats and the ginger ale we stole from the nursing station. We trudged down to the ER and knocked on the patient's door. My senior asked for her chief complaint, but she didn't answer. She put her hand on the patient's chest and she didn't move. You wouldn't believe it, Aerik. She was dead! It was absolutely unbelievable."

"What!" I said incredulously. "The ER asked you to admit a dead patient?"

"Yes! But get this, the only thing my senior resident cared about was getting credit for the admission. She was so tired that she had no concern for the patient's death."

"What!" I repeated. "You can't get credit for admitting someone who's dead. That's bullshit."

"Yes, but the patient wasn't dead when they asked us to admit her. She was only close to death. We started the process of the admission as soon as the ER called. Therefore, since admission efforts were started while the patient was alive, my senior demanded credit for the admission."

"Well that's a tough one," I said. "I see your point. The admission started while the patient was alive, but technically the admission wasn't completed. Therefore, I would imagine that the admission didn't count?"

"That's logical," she said. "But there is no language in the ACGME rule book that speaks directly to admitting dead people. Our argument was that the ACGME protects us from physician fatigue. As we had already started the admission paperwork, the physician fatigue had begun. It would violate the spirit of the ACGME to not give us credit for the admission and expect additional physician fatigue with a future admission."

I gave it some thought. It sounded reasonable to me. They had reached their maximum with a dead patient!

Imagine that. Someone's wife just died, and two residents are discussing whether ACGME rules would be violated if not given admission credit. I had become hardened by the process.

During my surgical rotation as a third-year medical student, I had the privilege of being on trauma call at Grant Hospital. I call it a privilege because Grant Hospital is where my father performed his family practice residency. His senior class picture hangs outside the auditorium. I found myself stopping and staring at that picture with every pass through the hallway. He wore a clean-cut afro and had a big grin on his face. It made me feel proud and it gave me determination. It was also a pleasure to rotate at Grant Hospital because it is a

Level I trauma center, which means they accepted everything. Gunshot wounds, stabbings, motor vehicle accidents, blunt force trauma—they saw it all. As an eager third-year medical student, I was excited for trauma call. I met with my senior resident on the first call day and he gave me his expectations: "Show up on time and don't sleep through the pager," he said. Then he walked away.

"Is there anything I should read to prepare myself?" I asked.

"Just be prepared for anything. We won't be asking you many questions. This isn't Internal Medicine. You will learn by doing. It will move pretty fast." His back was to me while he was talking, on his way down the corridor.

I went up to my call room full of excitement. I had transformed from a timid medical student into one who couldn't wait to get involved. I picked up my surgery review textbook and went to the trauma section. I read for thirty minutes and then checked my pager. I had no pages. I read for another hour and checked my pager. Still there was no action. "Damn," I said to myself. "When are the traumas coming?" Hours passed by and my pager was silent. I remember checking the batteries to make sure it was working. The anxiety was building and I couldn't take it anymore. I walked down to the trauma bay around midnight. The rooms were spotless, the instruments were neatly tucked away, and the beds were robed with clean sheets.

"Nothing yet, young doc," said one of the nurses. "We'll let you know." I retreated back to my call room and drifted to sleep. I awoke in angst at 3:00 a.m. and checked my pager. There was still no action. Just my luck. Slow trauma night during my first call. I picked up my surgery review book. I had read it over at least twice. I've always prided myself in being prepared. No sooner than I dozed off with book in hand, my pager went off.

I leapt from the bed and ran to the bathroom to throw some water on my face. "Wake up!" I said to myself. I looked in the mirror. My eyes were red and droopy. The crease lines from my pillow were indented in my face. I smelled a musty odor coming from my armpits. I hadn't showered in the past twenty-four hours. I looked like I had aged ten years since the start of medical school. I grabbed my stethoscope and white coat and sprinted down the breezeway as fast as I could. I reached the trauma bay breathing heavily and in a mild sweat to find the nursing and medical staff making their preparations. I caught a glimpse of my senior resident, who was confidently twirling trauma shears in his hands with ease. "Hey, young doc," said one of the nurses. "Gunshot wound to the left thorax. Vital signs are unstable. He'll be here shortly."

I nodded my head. I had nervous energy. My hands were shaking and my mind was racing. It reminded me of the hours prior to a collegiate soccer game. Soccer was easy. Once the game started the nervousness went away and reflexes took over. In the trauma bay, however, I had no idea what I was doing. I had yet to develop reflexes. I had only read the book.

Reflexes develop with time and practice. Third-year medical students are very smart until somebody faints in front of them. We have information stored in our brains from years of studying textbooks, but processing this information and acting in a relevant and concise manner is challenging. It is not an innate response.

"A and then B and then C," my senior said to me. "Got it?"

He's right, I thought. This doesn't have to be difficult. Assessing an acutely ill patient in a systematic fashion involves first assessing the Airway and then Breathing, followed by Circulation. It's one of the first things you learn in medical school. "Got it!" I said confidently. "I'll assess his airway first and then his breathing. After which I will assess his circulation."

"No, Aerik. I'll assess his airway and breathing. You need to put your finger in his Anus and then put the urinary catheter in his Bladder." He chuckled to himself. Nothing like a little medical student humor. I didn't care. My skin had thickened since my Internal Medicine rotation. If my senior resident wanted me to do the rectal exam, then I'll be damned if I didn't do the best rectal exam in the history of Ohio State Medicine. Besides, it's important to assess rectal tone in the setting of trauma and I was happy to be a part of the team. I grabbed a mask with a plastic shield that extended to protect my face. A nurse helped me put on a surgical gown. I put on some gloves, grabbed the lube for the rectal exam, and put the catheter kit on a nearby table.

The call came in over the speaker that the ambulance was two minutes away. We had a team of about ten. All were gowned in shiny blue protective clothing with mesh-like slippers over our shoes to protect us from the bodily fluids that would soon spill. The trauma surgeon and chief resident were fixing their clinical scrub caps around their heads. All of their movements were methodical from years of experience. The air was a bit tense. There was less chatter as the time elapsed. In the middle of the room was a surgical table with a bright adjustable light above. Nothing seemed to be out of order.

I never heard the ambulance. I just remember the doors opening suddenly. BAM! An EMS team member was yelling at the top of his lungs while pushing a patient on a stretcher. "Twenty-eight-year-old African American male with a gunshot wound to the left thorax. There is an obvious contusion to the base of his skull. We have a blood pressure of 80 by palpation and a heart rate of 160." Two EMS team members quickly rolled the patient's stretcher towards the surgical table. He had a tube sticking out of his mouth that extended into his trachea from successful intubation while en route. A bag was attached to the intubation tube, and an EMS member was squeezing the bag to deliver oxygen to the victim's lungs. He was supported by a backboard. On the count of three, two EMS members lifted the patient by the backboard and dropped him onto the surgical table. Then they left. As quickly as they arrived, they were gone. It was our turn now.

With an impeccable maneuver, the chief resident sliced all of the victim's clothing with his trauma shears. Two nurses worked in tandem to apply electrocardiogram leads so that his heart rate and rhythm could be monitored, and another nurse placed a blood pressure cuff on his arm. "We need two large-bore IVs!" yelled the chief. The nurses had already started working on placing the peripheral venous lines before he barked his command. The victim's veins were flat from his low volume state. He had lost liters of blood before arriving to the Emergency Department. He was alive but in critical condition. The respiratory technician attached the intubation tube to the ventilator machine. "We need IV access," the senior demanded again. The nurses were having difficulty obtaining intravenous lines, so a second-year resident quickly grabbed a central line kit. She cleaned the right groin with Betadine and stuck a large bore needle with an attached syringe into his femoral vein. She pulled back on the plunger and dark venous blood began to fill the syringe. She removed the syringe and slid a wire through the opening of the needle. Next, she took a catheter and ran the opening through the wire, which allowed the catheter to settle perfectly within the femoral vein.

"We have venous access!" she shouted. Type O negative blood and normal saline fluid were infused through the catheter. The ABCs, I thought to myself. The airway was secured and the ventilator was delivering oxygen to his lungs. His circulation was still an issue. We had a mechanism to deliver blood and saline fluids through the femoral catheter; however, the problem was that he had lost liters prior to transport. The only way to keep up would be to stop the bleeding.

It was my turn. I grabbed some lube and slathered my index finger. I couldn't see his rectum, so I had to feel for it. "It's higher up than you would think," the second-year resident told me. After a few embarrassing seconds, I found it and I slid my finger inside. If you or I were to have pressure put on the skin surrounding the anus, the anal sphincter muscles would contract, a phenomenon known as the perineal reflex. The absence of this reflex is indicative of damage to the nervous system.

"No perineal reflex. Absence of rectal tone," I shouted. I changed my gloves and then opened the urinary catheter kit. I put lubrication on the catheter, grabbed the victim's penis, and pushed the catheter through the urethral opening and into his bladder. A bright stream of yellow urine filled the catheter bag. My job was done. It was time to watch and learn. The senior resident and trauma surgeon were busy at work trying to stop the bleeding, but it was futile. His blood pressure continued to drop, and within minutes, his heart stopped. He was dead.

The room looked like a blood bath. The once immaculate blue gowns were stained with blood and yellow fat that spilled following the surgical incisions. Protective slippers covered our shoes from the blood clots splattered on the floor. There were surgical instruments strewn across the bed. The bright light that shone on the victim was causing beads of sweat to roll down my brow and armpits.

The senior resident emphatically extended his index finger towards me. "Start chest compressions!" I interlocked my fingers on the patient's chest and pumped as hard as I could. Within seconds my arms began to tire. I internally begged for the patient to respond. I fixated on his eyes which were glazed over, oscillating with each compression. He had no voluntary control. My concentration then drifted to his abdomen. He had a tattoo of a handgun and a phrase written in a cursive font just below his belly button. I couldn't quite make out the entire phrase because it was covered in blood, but the last words read "Bone Thugs." The surgery attending recognized my exhaustion.

"Someone switch with Aerik!" he yelled.

I gladly retreated to the front of the table while the second-year resident continued compressions. I couldn't help but wonder if the victim was a gang member given the tattoo. Inexplicably, I began to hum the lyrics of "Crossroads" by Bone Thugs-N-Harmony.

"Now tell me, what ya gonna do
When it ain't nowhere to run
When judgment comes for you
When judgment comes for you
Now tell me, what ya gonna do
When it ain't nowhere to hide
When judgment comes for you
'Cause it's gonna come for you"

What the hell was I doing? Why didn't I care? I remember being so fatigued that the only thing I could think of was going back to bed. The senior resident called the time of death at 3:45 a.m.

The Eighth Floor

I felt like a seasoned doctor just a few months into my third year of medical school. The fear and anxiety of looking stupid was replaced with cockiness. On the surgery service I carried around a needle driver and spun it effortlessly in my hands, a trick I learned from a senior resident. "What are you applying for?" a resident asked me. All medical students must pick a field of medicine to practice by their fourth year of school.

"I don't know. I haven't narrowed it down yet."

"You want to cut?" That was slang for asking if I wanted to be a surgeon. Before I could answer, he smugly stated, "I already know you want to cut."

He didn't know anything. I hadn't narrowed down my options. I was enjoying my surgery rotation, but it was exhausting, and the surgeons were so irritable. I couldn't imagine sustaining that lifestyle for my entire career. Would I turn irritable myself if I became a surgeon? When would I have time for family? When would I have time for self? I could barely find time to go to the bathroom. I would arrive to the surgical floors at 4:30 a.m. to round on patients by myself to ensure I was prepared for house-staff rounds, which started at 5:30 a.m. The first surgery case was at 7:00 a.m., and cases ran

44

until the early evening. I was on call every fourth night, which meant I wouldn't get home until late. When I did arrive home, I would microwave my dinner and then pass out on the couch. Weekends were similar to weekdays. I understood why surgeons were so testy. I didn't want to become that person.

One attending in particular personified the stereotypical surgeon. He took every opportunity to insult the medical student, the nurse, the fellow, even the janitor. One evening, just before leaving the hospital after a full day in the operating room, a young woman came into the emergency department with abdominal pain. A CT scan of the abdomen showed possible appendicitis. Her white blood cell count was elevated and she had a fever. The attending was filled with anger, but not because he was two steps out of the door before his day was prolonged with a last-minute appendectomy. He loved the operating room and would prefer to spend every waking second with a scalpel in his hand. He was angry because he knew immediately that the ER physician had the wrong diagnosis. "Aerik. I want you to know that a young woman with abdominal pain, an elevated white blood cell count, and fever is more likely to have pelvic inflammatory disease than appendicitis. I bet those assholes didn't even do a pelvic exam."

We went to the patient room in the Emergency Department to meet the young woman. "Good evening, ma'am. My name is Dr. Beeker. How do you do?"

"I've been better, sir," she said, guarding her belly with her arms in obvious discomfort.

"Do you have sex?" he asked her matter-of-factly.

"Excuse me, sir?" she said dramatically, emphasizing each syllable.

"Do you have sexual intercourse?" I guess that was his attempt at clarification. She was stunned. He went all the way from "How do you do?" to "Do you have sex?" in a matter of seconds. That's one of those questions that you ease into. Dr. Beeker had no touch.

"Yes, sir. I'm sexually active." She was part blushing and part disgusted by his bedside manner. Little did she know, it was about to get worse.

"How many partners?" Dr. Beeker asked.

"My goodness!" she said. "Why are you asking me these questions?" Dr. Beeker didn't respond and just waited for an answer. You wouldn't believe how uncomfortable the next fifteen seconds of silence were. "Just my boyfriend," she said finally.

"He may be cheating on you then," said Dr. Beeker. "I need to talk to your Emergency Room doctor and I'll be back." Then we left without giving her any explanation as to the presumption of infidelity.

I imagined her still lying there trying to figure out what the hell just happened. Dr. Beeker began marching around in a rage. "Who is seeing the patient in room seven?" he yelled so that the entire ER could hear him. Everyone stopped what they were doing and sat quietly. It was as if they knew he was about to go apeshit. He had obviously done it before.

"I'm seeing her," an ER physician said in a meek voice towards the end of the nursing station. The color from his face drained as Dr. Beeker approached with me in tow.

"I reviewed the CT scan. I don't see appendicitis!" Dr. Beeker's voice was rising to a crescendo.

"Well, the radiologist was concerned that there may be some inflammation around the appendix. That's why we called you," the ER doc said in a mild-mannered tone.

"Well, I reviewed the CT scan myself and there is no inflammation," Dr. Beeker snapped back. "I was taught to read CT scans in medical school. Aerik, are they still teaching medical students to read abdominal CT scans in medical school?" he asked me.

I wanted to stay out of this battle, but Dr. Beeker put me square in the middle. "Yes, sir," I lied. I didn't know the first thing about reading a CT scan of the abdomen, but lying seemed to be a better option at the time.

"Did you see any inflammation when you reviewed the CT scan, student doctor Williams?" He emphasized the word "student."

"No, sir. I didn't see any inflammation." I technically wasn't lying this time. I didn't see any inflammation because I didn't know what inflammation on a CT scan looked like.

"Well, the student didn't see any inflammation on the CT scan either," said Dr. Beeker, emphasizing the word "student" once again. "You must be confused!" he snapped.

The ER doc sat motionless. He looked like a kid being scolded by his father. Dr. Beeker's face was flaming red and he was about to burst at the seams.

"Student doctor Williams, you will be taking your basic medical school surgery exam at the end of this rotation. If there is a question about a sexually active young woman with fever, abdominal pain, and elevated white blood cell count, would you choose appendicitis as your answer?"

"No, sir." That's when it dawned on me that when Dr. Beeker told me earlier that young women with a elevated white blood cell count and abdominal pain are less likely to have appendicitis, he was prepping me for this moment. "I would be concerned for pelvic inflammatory disease," I said.

"Ah. What a sage student you are." He was now mocking the ER attending. He knew damn well what he was doing. He staged the entire thing. "Did you do a pelvic exam?" he asked the ER attending. Dr. Beeker already knew the answer. There was no pelvic exam documented in the patient's chart.

"No, I didn't," he said, now completely embarrassed.

Then at the top of his lungs, Dr. Beeker shouted, "Then maybe you should perform a pelvic exam so that we don't have to cut open her abdomen unnecessarily!"

Dr. Beeker always seemed irritable. All he had to do was tell the ER doc to perform a pelvic exam when he was called with the consult and we would have avoided all this nonsense. Encounters like this are what pushed me away from general surgery. I didn't want to become Dr. Beeker.

The pelvic exam was performed, and Dr. Beeker was correct. She had pelvic inflammatory disease.

Even if I didn't become an asshole, I knew the fatigue and heavy workload would pull me away from my family. I spent a year after college working in a transplant laboratory at Johns Hopkins. The head surgeon in the lab was old school. He spent hours in the operating room. When he wasn't in the operating room, he was in clinic. When he wasn't in clinic, he was in the lab directing research. When he wasn't directing research, he was giving talks on his research on campus. When he wasn't giving talks on his research on campus, he was traveling all over the world to give talks on his research. When did he see his family? His wife called the lab looking for him on occasion. Was she comfortable not seeing her husband? When she did see him, was he too exhausted to hold a conversation?

My last month of surgery rotation was spent on the vascular surgery service. The intern on the service was always absent. He would show up to the hospital just in time for morning rounds, though typically unprepared, and then he would disappear. Interns are first-year residents, and at this hospital, they rarely went into the operating room. Their job was to ensure that all responsibilities for patients on the hospital floor were met. They wrote discharge instructions, arranged for patients to have physical therapy after their hospital stay, admitted patients from the emergency department, answered all nursing questions, etc. It was busywork, less onerous than senior resident responsibilities in the operating room. If all was calm on the surgery floor, my intern would make his way to the call room and catch a nap. He was always silent on rounds without anything intelligent to add. He would nod his head as I presented patients as if he were in agreement. Truth be told, had I called in sick, he wouldn't have had a clue as to why patients were even in the hospital.

As a student, I was unable to write medical orders, which meant the intern would have to log into a patient's chart and key in the orders himself. Because my intern was never anywhere to be found, I would have to page him. "What?" he would answer when returning a page, as if I was annoying him.

"The attending wants a Doppler ultrasound in bed 120. Can you put in the order?" I returned. He wouldn't verbally acknowledge my request, rather just hang up the phone. I know he heard me because eventually the order would be placed. I was always curious as to where he found refuge from the vascular unit, but I minded my own business. He would write an end-of-the-rotation evaluation, so I wanted to stay in his good graces. I found it peculiar, however, that he always returned phone calls from the eighth floor in a building adjacent to the vascular center. In between cases one afternoon, I found myself without much work to do. I paged the intern and asked if he would like to meet for lunch. I wanted to kiss his ass since he would be writing my evaluation. He answered the page from the eighth floor.

"I can't, man. I'm busy seeing patients," he said abruptly. I knew that was bullshit. We didn't have any patients on the eighth floor. I decided to see exactly what preoccupied his time. I took the elevator up to the eighth floor and stepped onto a ward unlike any of the others. The intern was lounging at the nursing station, surrounded by a few young, beautiful nurses. He was smiling, showing off his pearly whites, spinning around in his chair. He was talking about everything other than patient care. He had pulled up the sleeves of his scrub top to accentuate his little muscles. He probably did some push-ups in the call room before heading up to see his "patients." I wasn't mad at him; I just felt ambivalent. I turned towards the elevator and headed to the cafeteria.

I only had a few days left on the vascular service. It was early in the morning and I was in the library studying the anatomy of the femoral triangle in preparation for a femoral popliteal bypass surgery. It's a procedure to treat femoral artery plaque disease by creating a conduit around the plaque. It's similar to how cars are rerouted when a car accident obstructs the highway. The drivers leave the highway an exit before the accident, bypass the accident by taking the side streets, and return to the highway once the path is clear. In this procedure, the surgeon takes a vein that has been stripped from the patient and creates an alternate route for blood flow around the plaque.

I left the library to see the patient in the preoperative suite. His name was Benny. He was a young man in his early forties, easily the youngest patient I had seen on service. Unfortunately, he had a family history of peripheral vascular disease and he smoked two packs of cigarettes per day. This is a very dangerous combination. The plaque in his femoral artery reduced blood flow to his left lower leg, which resulted in severe pains when walking. Without this surgery, he would eventually lose his leg. He had no questions for me; he just advised that I never smoke cigarettes.

I knew the procedure well. I had assisted on several femoral artery bypass surgeries that month that were all routine without complications. The surgeon made an incision and dissected down to the femoral artery. The artery was pinched with clamps to transiently inhibit blood flow. Once the artery was clamped, the clock started. The saphenous vein must be sewn into the artery at points before and after the plaque. There is no rush per se; however, there is urgency to finish this part of the bypass procedure given the clamp is preventing blood flow to the lower extremity. Only once the vein is sewn in place are the clamps released and the blood flow restored.

The attending vascular surgeon was a rounded man with a thick accent. He immigrated from India and had been practicing at the hospital for decades. He never took himself too seriously and was an attending that medical students enjoyed. He liked to play jokes on students to get us off our game. That's why I thought he was kidding when he asked for a surgical instrument of which I was unfamiliar following the clamping of the artery. The nurses were also taken by surprise. "Dr. Haque, we don't have such an instrument." His typical playful demeanor turned into anger.

"What do you mean you don't have it?" he demanded. "It's on my card!" The card refers to the list of surgical instruments a particular surgeon requires while in the operating room. Because surgeons have different styles and techniques, the instruments on the cards will vary depending on the surgeon.

"Dr. Haque, it's not on your card," the nurse said meekly.

"God damn it! We have an artery clamped!" Dr. Haque was furious. It was obvious this wasn't one of his jokes. I stood there motionless. "And it is on my card!" he barked.

One of the nurses sprinted out of the room and returned seconds later with the instrument. She had grabbed it from a set intended for another surgeon. "Thank you!" he said, still clearly agitated. "And if it's not on my card, then put it on my card." The operating room exploded with laughter. He recognized that he was being an ass and made a self-deprecating joke. He kicked me from underneath the table, which forced me to make eye contact. He winked. I was sure he was laughing under his mask.

The surgery was otherwise uneventful. Dr. Haque allowed me to sew up the skin incision. It was a slow process. I could barely keep my eyes open because of fatigue. I was tired as hell. "I think the fibroblasts will heal the incision faster than your stitching." He patted me on the back and walked out of the operating room. Fibroblasts are cells in connective tissue that produce collagen, which allows for a wound to heal naturally over the course of many days.

Sign-out was at 5:00 p.m. I wasn't on call so that meant I could go home. I went to check in on Benny before I left the hospital. He had been extubated after the surgery and by the nursing accounts had no complaints. "What's up, man?" I've never been formal with patients.

"Hey, doc."

"You been doing okay?" I asked. He had sweat on his brow and was a bit nauseated.

"I'm doing just fine. Thanks for all your help."

"My pleasure, man. I'll see you tomorrow."

"Just one thing, doc," he said as I was reaching for the door. "I've got a weird feeling in my chest. Feels like a little bit of pressure. I've had it before. Is that normal after surgery?"

"It may be related to your nausea, but I'll let the intern know. See you in the morning."

I headed over to the nursing station for sign-out. The intern came rolling in, smiling with visions of the eighth floor in his head.

"Hey, man. I'm signing out. Can you go see Benny for me? I think he needs an electrocardiogram and troponin levels. He was complaining of some chest pressure and nausea. May just be typical post-operative stuff."

"Sure. No problem," he told me. We'd developed mutual respect by the end of the month. Senior team members can develop respect and trust for medical students, but it must be earned. I figured I was doing a good enough job if he was talking to me. I went home and crashed. I had no dinner, just slept. General surgery was not in my future. I didn't have the surgeon personality. I certainly couldn't stay up long hours without becoming a complete asshole.

I awoke the next morning at 4:15 a.m., grabbed my white coat, and headed out the door. I was counting down the days left on the vascular surgery service. I was tired of being tired. I went straight to Benny's room for the standard postoperative conversation and physical exam, but upon entering, I recognized immediately something was wrong. Benny was intubated. The respiratory technician was adjusting Benny's ventilator settings. A powerful anesthetic called propofol was dripping through the IV catheter and into a vein in his arm for the purposes of sedation. "What's up with Benny?" I asked.

"He was having difficulty breathing last night," the respiratory technician said. "They checked a chest X-ray and he had some fluid in his lungs. He developed respiratory alkalosis, so we had to intubate him."

I pulled up Benny's electronic chart on the computer in his room. I scrolled down the screen to look at his troponin level, which I asked the intern to order the day prior. It was elevated at 25 ng/ml. Troponin is an enzyme that leaks into the blood when there is damage to the heart muscle. Small elevations of troponin are not uncommon in several noncardiac conditions; however, a level of 25 ng/ml is very high and very concerning. I pulled up the electrocardiogram on the screen and recognized "ST segment" changes, which are associated with damage to the heart. Benny had a heart attack. The nausea, chest pressure, and sweating that I observed the day prior were all associated symptoms. The chart was otherwise empty, which was a bit strange. If there was medical management for a heart attack, it should have been documented with patient notes and recorded in the chart. Certainly there was medical management? I remember being unmoved. I was sure there was a good reason for the lack of documentation. On to the next patient ...

At 5:30 a.m., the vascular surgery team met at the nursing station for house staff rounds. "Let's start with Benny," the senior vascular fellow stated.

I began: "The patient is a forty-year-old male with a past medical history of peripheral vascular disease. He is one day status post fem-pop bypass. His hospital course has been complicated by myocardial infarction approximately six hours post-operatively. He was intubated—"

"Hold it!" the senior fellow demanded. "What did you say?" There was an awkward silence. The atmosphere was tense. Did I make a mistake? Everyone was looking at me. The other medical students, the intern, the senior residents, the senior fellow, the nursing staff, and the respiratory team were all staring at me.

"He's a forty-year-old male, one day status post fem-pop bypass that had an acute cardiac event last night," I stated unconfidently. "He's intubated." My voice wavered as I pointed towards his hospital bed. The senior fellow peeked into Benny's room with a look of surprise. "The chest X-ray demonstrates he has some fluid in his lungs, likely from poor left ventricular function." There was a flurry of activity amongst the senior staff. The fellow grabbed the laptop away from the intern in order to view the electronic medical record. Other residents quickly sifted through the chart to find any evidence to support my conclusion.

"Last night you say he had a cardiac event?" the senior fellow questioned dubiously. I was intimidated. He was approximately six feet, six inches tall with a bulky frame, and in that moment, he looked like the Incredible Hulk. "What's his troponin?"

"It's twenty-five," I stated with growing confidence.

"You mean point 25?" he scoffed.

"No, sir. I mean twenty-five!" I realized the moment he found the lab result on the electronic medical record. I could see his pupils dilate.

"This was last night, you say? Where is the electrocardiogram?" A resident grabbed it from the chart and placed it in front of him. "Hmm … ST-segment changes. Did anyone else see this?" Now he was yelling. Nobody said a word. "When did you find out about this, Dr. Williams?" Whenever a senior physician calls a medical student "doctor" followed by their last name in the setting of an error, it's sarcasm. In actuality, he's saying, "When did you find out about this and why didn't you tell anybody, you dumbass?"

"He was having chest pressure, nausea, and he was sweating yesterday at sign-out, so I told the intern."

Now one thing you should know about me is that I'm a snitch. I not a ride-or-die guy. I'm a get-the-hell-out-of-the-way guy. I'm not going down with the ship. I'm not taking responsibility for something that isn't my fault. I'll tell on your ass in a heartbeat. Had the Internal Medicine attending asked me who paged her to the Gay Men's Choir, Tone would have been expelled from medical school. I wouldn't have even felt bad about it. I'm all about self-preservation. It was the intern's fault. Had the electrocardiogram and troponin level been tattooed on the ass of the nurse on the eighth floor, we wouldn't be in this situation. But alas, it was recorded in Benny's chart in the vascular center, where the intern was supposed to be.

"You told the intern?" the vascular fellow asked me.

"Yesterday before I left, I told the intern." I stared at the intern. He was embarrassed and mad as hell. I didn't care. Benny had a heart attack that started approximately twelve hours prior and nobody knew. If nobody knows, then there is no intervention note in the chart … because you can't do an intervention if nobody knows that you're supposed to intervene. You only know if you're supposed to intervene if you're paying attention. The intern was paying attention to the tight-fitting scrubs on the eighth-floor nurses. Benny died later that week.

I received my surgery grade soon after Benny's death. In the "comments" section, there was mild criticism of my inability to follow up with lab results, a clear reference to Benny. I didn't care at all because I received an "Honors" score. "Yes!" I shouted. "I got honors!"

The Impasse

I performed my Internal Medicine internship and residency at Thomas Jefferson Hospital, which is a fantastic place to train. The city of Philadelphia is wide and diverse, which exposes trainees to a variety of pathology. Because of its standing, hospitals in the outskirts of Philadelphia that treat lower acuity patients transfer complex cases to Thomas Jefferson.

One evening during my intern year, my senior resident and I were in the lounge with our fingers crossed. A patient transferring from an outside hospital was to appear on the intensive care unit within the hour, and the only information we had was that the patient was septic. Sepsis is defined by an inflammatory response to an infection. The inflammatory mediators released into the body during sepsis can cause blood pressure to drop, which is an ominous sign. Reduction in blood pressure reduces blood flow to all bodily organs, which can lead to organ failure. According to the Centers for Disease Control and Prevention, one in every three patients that die in the hospital has sepsis.[3] There are different levels of sepsis, categorized by severity. We were hoping for a less severe case.

The nurse sent a page once the patient arrived on the floor. He was a very nice and soft-spoken elderly man I believed to be in his seventies. He had a history of coronary artery disease and had bypass heart surgery in the past. His heart function was on the low end of normal. Reduced blood flow to his heart in his septic state could yield devastating consequences. Given the cardiac expertise at our hospital, the decision was made to transfer. The nurses at the outside hospital had already placed two peripheral venous lines and normal saline fluid was running through his veins. I reviewed the antibiotic sensitivities to the bug that was growing in his blood. After careful consideration, I choose an appropriate antibiotic. His blood pressure was tenuous and therefore the decision was made to start him on a medication called Levophed. This drug causes the blood vessels to constrict, similar to adrenaline, and is used to increase blood pressure in the setting of sepsis. Infusing Levophed through a peripheral intravenous line is controversial. If the Levophed leaks and is not delivered directly into the vein, the patient may have local tissue injury. Therefore, infusing Levophed through a central line is preferred.

Central lines access veins that are larger and deeper than veins that are visible in the skin. Gaining central line access is a sterile procedure that requires practice and skill. Anatomical landmarks and ultrasound imaging are used to locate the central veins. A large bore needle gains access to the vein and then a guide wire is thread through the opening of the needle until it rests in the vein. The needle is then removed and a catheter is threaded through the guide wire and sewn into place. Levophed can be administered through the catheter and into the central vein with less concern for tissue injury. There are risks to central line placement, including embolism, infection, hematoma, arrythmia, pneumothorax, catheter malposition, and arterial puncture, amongst others.

The case was discussed with the cardiology fellow and I was asked to place a central line with the guidance of the senior resident. The senior resident had the patient sign consent to place the central line. I put on a gown, sterile gloves, and a mask to protect my face. I opened a central line kit and was abruptly told to stop.

"What the heck are you doing?" yelled a woman unfamiliar to me. She put her hand on my shoulder with more force than necessary. Good thing I didn't have the needle in my hand.

"Excuse me, ma'am," I said respectfully. "I'm about to start a procedure. May I ask who you are?"

"You're not about to start anything. I'm Kathy, his daughter, and nobody informed me about any of this!"

Well, this was true. I didn't inform her about the central line, but I didn't have to. The patient was in his right state of mind and was oriented to all things around him. I didn't need his daughter's consent. "I'm sorry, ma'am. I asked your father and he signed consent."

"None of this is necessary! He didn't have a central line at the other hospital. Why does he all of a sudden need one now? He comes to this hospital and you want to do everything differently. You are only supposed to be monitoring his heart while his sepsis is being treated with antibiotics. The blood culture grew E. coli. Just treat it with the correct antibiotic and monitor him."

"Ma'am, his blood pressure is at the low end of normal," I said in a tone trying to create a sense of calm. "I have discussed this case with the cardiology fellow, and we are in agreement that given his underlying heart disease, he would benefit from Levophed. In order to put him on Levophed, he—"

She interrupted me again. "I know. He must have a central line to be put on a pressure."

"Ma'am, Levophed is called a pressor, not a pressure," I said with a hint of cynicism.

It became very apparent that Kathy was misinformed, but she was adamant in driving her father's care.

"Did you say you talked to the cardiology fellow?" I knew exactly where she was going. "If you're not the fellow, then you're certainly not the attending. Who are you?"

"My name is Dr. Williams. I'm the intern on the team."

"Absolutely not!" Kathy exclaimed. "If my father needs a central line, it will not be put in by the intern."

"Ma'am, I have not had any complications from putting in central lines," I said.

"Well, how many of these have you done?" she asked.

"Three," I said meekly.

"Absolutely not!" she blurted again. "You haven't had any complications because you've only done three!"

I technically wasn't being dishonest when I told her I hadn't had any complications, but I didn't give her full disclosure that I had only started performing the procedure a few months ago. By the end of my residency, I placed no less than forty central lines with only one complication when I aspirated blood from the internal carotid artery.

"I demand to speak with the attending." Kathy had her arms crossed and her brow furrowed.

"The attending is at home. Can I help you?" the cardiology fellow said as he entered the room, alerted of our conversation by the charge nurse.

"Who are you?" Kathy asked suspiciously.

"Dr. Reid. I'm the cardiology fellow on call this evening. May I help you?"

"You can help me by calling the supervising attending."

"We will not be calling the supervising attending this evening. This is a teaching hospital. I am running the cardiology service," he said with a half-smile. His smile was never a real smile. It resembled more of a smirk. It was the type of smirk that alerted everybody that he was the smartest guy in the room. And he *was* the smartest guy in the room. "Dr. Williams will be putting in the central line." I felt an overwhelming amount of pressure all of a sudden.

"Dr. Williams is an intern! He's only performed three central lines!" snapped Kathy.

"Dr. Williams"—he was now staring at me—"do you feel comfortable putting in central lines?"

"Yes," I said confidently. I didn't feel confident. I felt the pressure to not screw up a procedure that I had performed only three times.

"Very good," said Dr. Reid. "Today will be his fourth central line."

The patient seemed to be calm throughout the discourse. He allowed his daughter to dictate his care. She was certainly energized to argue, even with a senior cardiology fellow at an academic hospital. Though the patient was calm, his cardiac rhythm was not. As we continued the conversation, I noticed that he began to have runs of ventricular tachycardia, signaling that the sepsis and hypotension were beginning to affect his heart. I could tell that my senior resident took notice as well.

"There is no way Dr. Williams will be putting in a central line in my father's neck!" Kathy snapped. Dr. Reid looked down at the floor for a few seconds before responding.

"Then we are at an impasse," he stated very calmly and began to walk out of the room.

"Dr. Reid," the resident stated. "He is having ectopy."

Dr. Reid took notice of the irregular rhythm. "We need to put that central line in now." He peered at Kathy and she didn't budge. Nobody was saying anything. We were all just staring at each other with occasional glances at the telemetry monitor to observe the patient's abnormal cardiac rhythm.

My goodness, I thought to myself. Are we gonna let this man have a heart attack over a pissing contest? Why is this nonsense taking precedence over patient care?

"Fine," said Kathy. "The senior resident can place the central line, but it will not be Dr. Williams. You must be by his side in case he needs help."

"That sounds like a plan," said Dr. Reid with a grin that signaled accomplishment.

Good thing he didn't die! I thought to myself.

An Awful Death

One late evening, while rotating as the senior resident on the oncology service, I was asked to evaluate a patient for admission from the Emergency Department. I was told the patient was a "train wreck" who was "circling the drain."

The second definition of "train wreck" in Merriam-Webster's dictionary is "an utter disaster or mess: a disastrous calamity or source of trouble." In medicine, we have borrowed this definition to define patients with many complicated medical problems. They are "a mess" or "a source of trouble." They will need constant attention. The time spent caring for these "train wreck" patients is "disastrous" because it distracts physicians from other duties.

When one flushes the toilet, the contents within revolve in a descending circular motion until sucked into a hole and down a sewer pipe. It does take some time, but eventually all contents are discarded. A patient circling the drain refers to a "train wreck" who is sick enough to be continuously admitted into the hospital, however not sick enough to die. The patient continues in declining health over the course of months until they are sucked out of this earth, just like the contents in your toilet bowl.

The "train wreck" had terminal cancer and was actively dying. I admitted him to the oncology unit, and I called the oncology fellow who relayed the message to the oncology attending. The family was gathered in the waiting room. I expressed my condolences and told them I would make their loved one as comfortable as possible during these final moments of his life. I pulled up the electronic medical record to order a morphine drip. This is a common end-of-life practice in order to prevent agitation. My pager went off before I could complete the order. It was the oncology fellow.

"The attending doesn't want you to start a morphine drip."

"Why the hell not?" I answered.

"He doesn't know whether or not the patient is actually dying."

"Well, why don't you tell him to get his ass in here and find out! Do you think I'm stupid? You don't think I know when someone is dying?" I was yelling at a senior fellow now and I didn't care. This back-and-forth went on for thirty minutes; meanwhile, there were audible gasps in the patient room. "Fuck it. I'm putting in the order." I walked into the patient's room to apologize for the delay. Can you imagine that? Apologizing for contributing to an uncomfortable death? I was frustrated and humiliated. When I walked into the room, the patient had already expired.

The Light

I do carry shame as I type these accounts. Shame for the disregard given to a dying man with a gunshot wound in the trauma unit. Shame for prioritizing admission credit over empathy for a deceased person in the emergency department. Shame for the ambivalence of Benny's death. Shame for allowing a pissing contest to affect a patient's cardiac rhythm. Shame for referring to patients as "train wrecks." The pastor tells me that I can leave this shame at the cross, but I still carry it deep in my heart.

I have experienced so much death and morbidity, I could have filled every page of this book. I became desensitized to death. My apathetic attitude paralleled some of my colleagues'. I lost sense of why I was on this earth. I wasn't depressed. I wasn't anxious. I wasn't angry. I was just tired and apathetic. You want to hear something disturbing? While in medical school, I used to play a game when I was driving home from the bar in the early hours of the morning. I would close my eyes and count to five while I was driving just to see what would happen. I was lost.

You know what's awesome? Despite all of this, there was a spirit that protected me. It took me many years to realize this fact. No matter how low I stooped, a spirit stood by me.

My daughter died less than twenty weeks in-utero during my residency. The pain of her death was unbearable but a blessing. My sadness was a blessing. My questioning of faith was a blessing. My tears were a blessing. Her precious few moments were a reminder that "people live like animals to die like angels—loved and wanted." What an awesome responsibility I have to provide a sense of love and worth to a person at their most vulnerable period. No matter the chaos in my life and no matter what others find to be acceptable, I will heed Pastor Furtick's message and look towards the Father for guidance.

I see it in my son. Our dog died in the spring of 2018. Good ol' Willa! She was a fat English bulldog with a white coat and a brown patch over her right eye. In her elder years, she developed arthritis and her playful interactions were few and far between. She walked with a very pathetic limp. In the final months, she lost one quarter of her body weight and vomited on a daily basis. She died one afternoon in our study. Her body rested in a very familiar position: her chest on the floor, hind legs curled up next to her butt, and head resting between her front legs. She used to sleep like this.

At the right moment, I broke the news to my seven-year-old son. This was his first dog. She was there when he was born and they would play together during his toddler years. They were good friends.

"Max, I have some sad news. Our dog passed away."

"Tyler died?" he said, referencing my childhood dog that he never met.

"No, Max. Willa passed away."

"You're kidding," he said with a big smile. You're tricking me." I regretted every time that I had been dishonest for the sake of laughter in the past.

"No, Max. I'm being serious. But it's okay. She was old and tired. She lived a wonderful life and she was loved by her family."

Max sat silently. The gravity of not being able to touch Willa again was setting in. "Well, I wish I could have said goodbye." He paused for a few seconds. "I wish I could have seen her for just a couple more days."

"Well, Max, we don't get to choose when the Lord takes us away." I gave him a hug, his soft cheeks pressed up to mine.

He gets it and I hope he never loses it.

Salud

I would like to introduce you to Julie. I met her when I was a senior resident working in the Bone Marrow Transplant Unit. She was a beautiful twentysomething. She had attractive long brown hair, big green eyes, and olive skin. Her smile was inviting and infectious. She was fun, more silly than serious.

She was diagnosed with leukemia as a teenager, many years before I met her. She was brave throughout. She was on and off chemotherapy, determined to beat her illness. She was a fighter. The thing about cancer though is that it's a fighter too, and cancer hates to lose. It's aggressive. Cancer is the bully that nobody wants to mess with. You can psych yourself up if you would like, but it will whip you even on your best day. I've seen it before. I saw a Philadelphia police officer swear he was going to beat leukemia. He was a real tough guy. He was also a cantankerous son of a bitch, the type that you don't want to meet in a dark alley. He underwent a bone marrow transplant. He had his arms folded and lips poked out. "Cancer won't beat me." He was dead within two months. Cancer ain't scared of nobody. It has no mercy for the meek. I've seen cancer rip right through reserved patients resigned to their fate.

Well, cancer hadn't met Julie. She was just as tough. She reminded me of Katniss Everdeen from *The Hunger Games*: determined, resourceful, and resolute. The odds were stacked against her, but she would manage to pull through. Her inner strength was inimitable. This would prove to be a heavyweight bout: cancer versus Julie. I was in Julie's corner.

Round one went to Julie. She knocked cancer straight on its ass. She had chemotherapy. She lost her hair. She lost her strength. She did NOT lose her will to live. She had resolve. She was back to being a teenager. She finished high school and went to college.

She was in remission and minding her own business when cancer got off the mat. It was time for round two. It came back undeterred with more vengeance and more power. The leukemia ravaged her body but not her spirit. Unable to handle this demon on her own, she called on the support of her family and friends. These beings aligned to create a supernatural spirit, one the likes that cancer had never seen before.

She was showered with love! Cancer hates love. It considers love to be its most prized possession. It strips loving families and friends apart, sending innocent people to early graves. But cancer was no match for the love in Julie's family or their supernatural spirit. She had more chemotherapy followed by a bone marrow transplant and again she won. She lost her hair. She lost her strength. She did NOT lose her will to live. Round two went to Julie.

She beat cancer ... twice. She was determined to live. Her immune system was a bit out of whack following the bone marrow transplant. She developed graft-versus-host disease of the skin, which is described by foreign transplanted cells attacking normal recipient cells. Her case was mild but would require oral steroids for an undetermined time. Otherwise, Julie was back to being Julie. Cancer got knocked on its ass ... again. It was out for the count.

Julie was cancer free and minding her own business when she developed a dry cough. No big deal, likely a viral infection, she was told. The cough, however, became progressive and eventually she developed shortness of breath and fatigue. She had difficulty with her normal activities. Gradually the cough and shortness of breath turned into fever and chest pain. When the chest pain was too much to bear, her mother brought her to the Emergency Department. A CT scan of the chest demonstrated miliary nodules and confluent parenchymal opacities. It was a pneumonia, but not your ordinary pneumonia. You see, when your immune system is weakened, it increases the opportunity to develop atypical infections. Julie's immune system was suppressed. This was not because of cancer or chemotherapy; she had beat this disease a few years prior. Julie was immunosuppressed because of the steroids she was taking daily to control graft-versus-host disease, a complication from her curative bone marrow transplant.

Julie was breathing in short bursts, and her oxygen levels were decreasing despite supplemental oxygen from a breathing mask. The ER team made the decision to intubate Julie and connect her to a ventilator machine that would breathe for her.

I met Julie about two weeks later, to my recollection. I never saw her long and attractive brown hair. It was stuck together in clumps and matted to her hospital bed. I never saw her big green eyes. There was a layer of film that kept them partially stuck together. I just imagined her this way. I imagined her to be friendly and jovial with an infectious smile. Just above the hospital bed was a picture of her with a group of friends in what appeared to be a dormitory room. I believe it was Halloween because everyone was dressed in costumes. Julie had on a blue wig, a cup in her hand, and she was smiling. The picture made her seem so distant from her current state. Only a few months before, she was drinking in her dorm room with friends, enjoying all of life's simple pleasures. Now she was intubated and talking over a breathing tube.

I was shaken and filled with sadness, but I needed to understand her clinical case. I reviewed her chart. Julie's respiratory cultures grew Coccidioides, an atypical fungus that lives in the soil in the southwestern United States. She was likely exposed to this fungus while visiting a friend in Arizona, as her cough started shortly after leaving. When people with healthy immune systems are exposed to Coccidioides, it is rendered innocuous. However, Julie's immunosuppressed state allowed the fungus to fester within her lung. The infection was eventually controlled with antifungal agents, but the inflammation from the infection caused irreversible lung damage. The pulmonary consult team had tried numerous times to extubate Julie, but every time the tube came out, Julie developed rapid breathing and her oxygen saturation would drop. This would yield the traumatic event of re-intubation. The opportunity for permanent extubation was minimal. She would be sent to a long-term facility where she would lie in bed on a ventilator with full cognition, separated from the outside world. Imagine being alone with your thoughts all day with the sound of the ventilatory machines in the background. Imagine that for the rest of your life.

Julie did summon the same support system that helped her beat cancer. They sang songs, held hands, and prayed for hours on end, but not even the supernatural spirit could restore her lung function. "I'm tired, Dr. Williams," she told me one morning on rounds. I could tell she had lost her will. I could tell she had lost her fight. I didn't know what to tell her. I had no cure. There was no medicine or intervention that could reverse her state. Her fate was sealed, and it was too much to bear. "I want to be extubated."

"Julie, you know we can't do that. We've tried several times, and the end result is putting the tube back into your trachea."

"I want you to take it out and I don't want you to put it back in," she whispered. She turned her head away from me to stare at the picture on the wall.

"Julie. You should take time to think about this. Perhaps with some time—"

She interrupted me. "No more time. I've been sitting here for long enough. The time has come."

If anyone knew the value of life, it was Julie. Her appreciation for this world was seen through the eyes of someone who had just recently clutched onto whatever she could in order to stay alive. Cancer had previously occupied her body and she stared at death in the eyes not once, but twice. After beating cancer, she had experienced the euphoria of life. To have it taken away from her was unbearable. "Tomorrow night," she said. "Eight o'clock in the evening."

I was stunned. I didn't blame her. I didn't try to persuade her. I just stood there. I felt I was looking right through her as if she were already dead. I called the psychiatry team to evaluate her. This is procedural. In order for anyone to make such a decision, they must be deemed competent, which she was. Eight o'clock tomorrow evening it was.

I arrived to the hospital the morning prior to her death and visited her before morning rounds. She was smiling, just like in her picture. Someone had wiped her face and brushed her long brown hair. I saw her big green eyes for the first time.

"Good morning, Dr. Williams," she said.

"Good morning, Julie."

She motioned to a man in the room. "This is my father." I hadn't met Julie's dad. In fact, it dawned on me that she had never mentioned him. I had plenty of conversations with her mom, but not her father. He was estranged. There was friction. I could feel it. She smiled and glowed as she talked about him. He wept and sobbed. His regret was palpable.

I had seen regret before on the oncology service. I met a man who had played poker his entire life at a competitive level. He had neglected his wife for years until she developed a very rare small bowel tumor. She had a terminal prognosis. He spoke about her in glowing terms until the last days. She just sat there emotionless as he littered her with adulation. In a private conversation while she lay dying in bed, her body riddled with tumors, she told me that he had never seemed to care until her final days.

Julie's friends and family had gathered by late afternoon. They smiled while they cried. They hugged. They laughed. They prayed. They brushed the hair from Julie's face with long strokes. They spoke of how much they loved each other. The eight o'clock hour approached. A beautiful death for Julie. She survived cancer and would die like an angel, loved and wanted.

I said my goodbye to Julie. I wasn't on call and therefore would not be there when she took her final breath. "Goodbye, Dr. Williams." We squeezed each other. I left the hospital with a saddened heart. I took the train home with my thoughts on Julie. The eight o'clock hour passed by, and I promise you I felt her ascend.

I arrived to the hospital early the next day, eager to see if Julie had changed her mind. She hadn't. The bed was empty with freshly pressed sheets and a pillow at its head, ready for the next patient. The floors had been wiped clean. The picture had been taken off the wall. The cardiac monitor was off and there was an open space that was once occupied by a ventilator. I thanked God for bringing her into my life. She taught me more about humility and death than my cumulative experience. It was time for me to get ready for morning rounds.

If it's not too much trouble, can you pause from reading this book? When you are at home and in your most comfortable chair with your mind free of distractions, please resume …

Thank you for your patience. If you wouldn't mind cleaning your favorite wineglass, no smudges or streaks. Now, a generous pour of your favorite wine and back to your comfy chair.

Are you there yet? Very good. I propose a toast.

Now tip your glass towards this book and I will tip mine towards you until they touch.

"To the beautiful being that Julie was and to her spirit that still lives in her mother."

Salud!

CHAPTER 2

Pimping

Throw in the Towel

We used to study at the law school library. There was nothing wrong with the medical school library. There were books. There were computers. The librarians were helpful. It had all things necessary for the academic development of the medical student. But the law school library had law school women. The medical school library had women too, but we had been staring at them all day in class. I was late to the discovery, but my buddy Tone filled me in.

"Bro, you gotta start studying at the law school library," he said.

"Why's that?"

"Bro, they've got law school ladies over there," he said. Tone still likes to start every sentence with "Bro."

"But we've got medical school and dental school ladies at our library," I said in retort.

"But Bro, you've been staring at 'Excuse me, professor' all day. This is different. You know Kafele's girl? He met her at the law school library." Tone was making a good point.

"Okay. I'll check it out. Better be good though. Don't waste my time, Tone."

"Bro, I promise. You'll be scooping girls up like you were playing shortstop!"

"Nice," I said. "Pick 'em up like a loose fumble and take it to the house?"

"Exactly!" said Tone. "Scoop and score."

So that's how I made my way to the law school library. As Tone had promised, there were law school women and they didn't seem to mind attention from medical students. The problem was that the librarian did not take kindly to our presence. She found every reason to come over to our table to bitch at us.

"Pick up your gum wrapper!"

"Ma'am, the gum wrapper will be thrown away when I leave."

"I'm going to need you to throw it away right now! You guys are always so loud when you come over here."

"Ma'am, I haven't said anything since I sat down."

"Well, I can hear you shuffling your papers and closing your books. If you don't quiet down, then you will need to leave!" she would say, pointing at the door.

My time at the law school library was short lived. It wasn't worth the hassle. The librarian wanted me out and I would oblige, but before my departure I overheard a conversation amongst a group of law students. A young woman appeared shaken and was being consoled by her colleagues. Earlier in the day she was berated by a law professor in front of her class for an error. She was an emotional catastrophe, sobbing like a baby with gobs of snot running down her face.

Law schools use something called the Socratic method as a teaching technique. This methodology is named after the philosopher Socrates. The premise is that argumentative dialogue between individuals sparks critical thinking. In law school, a student is asked a question in a public forum by a law professor. The student then answers the question and supports their position using assigned reading as their reference. The law professor then challenges the student's position. This challenge can take many forms. It can be benign without any attempt to embarrass the student but rather serve as an educational experience. The challenge can be malignant and yet still educational. Conversely, the challenge can be malignant and serve no educational purpose at all. The mood of the Socratic method is determined by the law professor. If the law professor is malignant, then one can expect a dialogue that is intended to embarrass the recipient of the questions. This is personified in the movie *The Paper Chase* where Professor Kingsfield gives a law student (James Hart) a dime, and in front of the entire class states, "Call your mother and tell her there is serious doubt about you ever becoming a lawyer." I believe the young lady in the law school library had a similar experience and her emotional fragility led to a breakdown.

I later came to find that attending physicians use the same technique on teaching rounds. We don't call it the Socratic method. We call it "pimping." Medical students are often asked the "pimp" question first during rounds. If their answer is insufficient, then the question is passed up the ranks to the intern. If the intern is unable to answer the question, it is then passed up to the senior resident. If the senior resident can't come up with the answer, it is then asked to the senior fellow. Pimpings can be difficult to prepare for because the list of potential medical questions is endless, but that's exactly what drives the student to leave no stone unturned when studying medicine. All information is important and at some point may be relevant. Therefore, comprehensive study is encouraged. In the end, it leads to better doctors. Similar to the Socratic method practiced in the field of law, pimpings can be educational or noneducational. They can also be benign or malignant, all dependent on the tone set by the attending physician.

I remember my first pimping as a medical student came on the Internal Medicine service. "Aerik, Ms. Taylor had shortness of breath overnight. What's in your differential diagnosis for acute shortness of breath in the hospitalized patient?" As if this question wasn't challenging enough for a newly minted third-year medical student, the entire team of nurses, social workers, co-medical students, and residents was staring at me waiting for an answer. I could feel my pulse increase and my palms start to sweat. I was unconfident and talked with such a soft tone that I could barely be heard. My preference has always been to remain silent and be thought a fool than to speak and remove all doubt. This approach, however, doesn't work when being pimped on Medicine rounds. "Speak up, please!" snapped the attending.

I came up with several potential diagnoses including pneumonia, myocardial infarction, and pneumothorax; however, I left out pulmonary embolism. Without the associated pressure, I'm sure I would have considered pulmonary embolism, but there's always some degree of pressure when practicing medicine. The attending scolded me, but appropriately so. It wasn't done with ridicule. It was educational. Pulmonary embolism has since been in my differential for acute onset shortness of breath, and I've diagnosed quite a few.

One of the most memorable pimp sessions that I witnessed was at Grant Hospital while on my general surgery rotation. Grand rounds were held in an auditorium. Medical students, nurses, nurse practitioners, residents, fellows, and attending physicians were all seated and the presenter stood in front of us at a podium. The room was pitch dark with the exception of a bright light that shone directly on the presenter. There was nowhere to hide. A second-year surgery resident was presenting a case on a patient with inflammatory bowel disease. Whether a patient with inflammatory bowel disease needs surgery is not always a clear-cut decision. The surgeons were contemplating surgical intervention.

The resident began presenting the case and we all listened intently. The patient had been admitted to the hospital several times in the past with abdominal pain secondary to his inflammatory bowel disease. The diarrhea, nausea, and abdominal cramping was debilitating. His disease led him to significant weight loss and a state of depression. He had tried several medications including the newer biopharmaceutical products to control his disease, but to no avail. The resident described the anatomy of his inflammatory lesions. They were scattered through the colon with the exception of the rectum. Because of the severity and recurrence of symptoms, the resident recommended complete surgical removal of the bowel as the next treatment strategy.

The attending questions that followed the presentation were typical. What would you see on X-ray if the patient had a perforation of his bowel? How many times must a patient's disease flare in order to consider surgery? Do resection margins and configuration of anastomosis increase the rate of recurrence of disease following surgery? The resident handled these questions with ease. His presentation was coming to a close and he was almost off the hook until one of the younger surgical attendings asked him a very basic question. In fact, I believe he asked the question to reinforce a concept important for the medical students in attendance.

"You haven't stated the type of inflammatory bowel disease the patient is suffering from. What type of inflammatory bowel disease does he have?"

This was the last question before we headed off to the operating rooms. It was a low-hanging fruit sort of question.

"What do you mean?" asked the resident. He looked perplexed but he knew well and good what the question was. We all heard the attending loud and clear. The resident was just buying time.

"What do you mean, what do I mean? The question was, what type of inflammatory bowel disease does the patient have?" the attending repeated.

"Well, he has evidence of inflammation in the colon, so it's certainly a colitis." This was obvious. I could tell he was going to struggle mightily. "As I said, the pathology demonstrates changes in the mucosal architecture with edema at different points in the colon. There is smooth muscle hypertrophy with numerous mast cells." Now he was starting to ramble. Nobody asked him about mast cells. Mast cells were as relevant as the man on the moon. He wasn't answering the question. The attending physician smelled blood. That's how pimping works. Once the recipient of the pimping demonstrates a weakness, there is an attack. In boxing we call it "working the cut." Once you've made your opponent bleed, you keep attacking the wound until he can't take anymore and his trainer throws in the towel.

"Do you know what type of colitis he has?" demanded the attending. "Yes or no!" He was growing tired of the resident's stalling.

"No," said the resident. His voice cracked. He had sweat beads on his brow. He removed his glasses to clear the fog.

"Well, what type of colitis do you think he has?" There was a deafening silence. "Think about it. Close your eyes and think about it."

The resident closed his eyes tightly. He looked like a fool standing up there with his eyes closed. He was squinting as if that would help the answer levitate into his brain. I couldn't help but giggle looking at the resident with his eyes closed. How embarrassing. This was exactly what the attending was trying to do, embarrass him. "You have the answer?" Of course he didn't.

"I don't know, sir." The resident slowly opened his eyes. If he had a white flag, he would have been waving it.

"Well, you reviewed the chart, I'm sure. You gave a fantastic presentation. Think about all of the facts you just laid out and tell me what type of inflammatory bowel disease he has. Take your time." The resident just stood there frozen. He could have had all the time in the world and he wouldn't have come up with the answer. If you haven't come up with an intellectual thought early in the pimp session, your chances of answering correctly are greatly diminished. Your brain becomes blocked. You're no longer thinking of an answer. You're just waiting for it to be over.

So we sat there in silence. Nobody was saying anything. One minute went by. Then two minutes went by. It seemed like an eternity. "Dr. Williams?" said the attending, breaking the silence.

"Yes, sir," I replied.

"Did you review the chart?"

"No, sir," I said. I didn't have to review the chart. It wasn't my patient and I had no idea this case was being presented.

"Can you tell me what type of inflammatory bowel disease the patient has?" I had to answer this question correctly because he had just called me "doctor" and he knew I was only a medical student. He was also breaking code. If I, a medical student, were to answer the question correctly in front of the resident's peers after the resident was unable to do so, this would cause humiliation. I, however, was licking my chops. I knew the answer and I love to grandstand.

"Crohn's disease," I said.

"Thank you!" he exclaimed as he glared at the resident, seemingly satisfied that the medical student had showed him up. "How did you come to such a conclusion?"

"I was told that the patient's disease spared the rectum." The resident's face drained of all color. He put his head down and sighed. The question wasn't a trick question. The question wasn't a difficult question. The attending just wanted to make the point that Crohn's disease is typically rectal sparing. We learn this in our first two years of medical school. It's on every board exam. The resident knew this, and if asked on any other occasion he would have come up with the answer. He got flustered on stage with the bright lights shining on him and the surgical department in the audience.

"Thank you, Dr. Williams." He motioned for the resident to step off the stage. He was downtrodden and clearly embarrassed.

"We are dismissed," said the chairman of surgery.

Now that was a pimp session. The resident certainly should have known the patient had Crohn's disease. I'm sure it was documented in the chart. Even if the resident hadn't read the chart, the fact that the disease spared the rectum should have given him a clue. Reinforcing this concept was appropriate. That's how we learn. I can assure you that the resident reviewed inflammatory bowel disease that evening. Making him stand up in front of the group with his eyes closed, however, was done for the purpose of ridicule.

Unit Float

Being an intern on the cardiology critical care service is daunting. The patients on this service are extremely sick. Small changes in the volume of blood in their circulatory system can lead to fluid accumulation in their lungs and reduce their heart's ability to pump blood to the rest of the body. Some patients have underlying coronary artery disease, which puts them at risk for a heart attack. There are patients who have heart rhythms that are irregular and need close monitoring. All of these patients require meticulous and detailed thought. It involves a thorough physical examination and careful study of electrocardiograms, echocardiograms, cardiac catheterization reports, laboratory values, etc.

I had anxiety when I stepped onto the cardiology critical care unit as an intern, and with good reason. Aside from the complexity of disease management, one of the attendings was a hard-ass who loved to pimp. His pimping fell into the ridicule category. Therefore, it was important to be ready for team rounds because he would be pimping relentlessly with the intent to humiliate.

Only a few days into the rotation, a physician interrupted our team rounds to alert us that he was sending a sick patient to the cardiology critical care unit. After discussing the case, he warned us that the patient had made racist comments in the past and was nearly kicked out of their cardiology practice for calling clinical staff "niggers." The critical care attending started to giggle. What a strange reaction, I thought to myself. Then with a wide smile he stated, "Maybe we should send Aerik in to see him."

Holy shit, I was angry. I was also scared. I wasn't necessarily scared of the attending. I was scared of what I was going to say. Had that been anywhere else, I would have dared him to repeat himself. I have some family from Newark, New Jersey, that would have dropped his ass on the spot. When Professor Kingsfield asked the law student to call his mother with the dime he was given, the law student responded with aggression. He called him a son of a bitch. I certainly felt that same aggression and that's what I was scared of. I wanted to challenge him, but I didn't. My word versus his. He was a senior attending. I would be labeled the troublemaker who couldn't take a "joke." Would my reputation be soiled and interfere with my ability to achieve a fellowship in the field of allergy and immunology? I swallowed my pride and I let it go. My only recourse was to document the interaction anonymously in his evaluation, which was probably never reviewed.

That sets the scene for the worst pimping that I've ever had. Two years later, and only a few months from residency graduation, I was a senior resident on the unit float service. Unit float residents cover the critical care service at night with the assistance of a junior resident and an intern. If I needed any backup, I would contact the on-call fellow, but as a senior resident I took pride in handling tough cases on my own. I was back in the cardiology critical care unit, and the attending who had jovially suggested that the black resident care for the racist patient was on service. I would have to present all new cases to him in the morning.

In the early evening hours, an obese male with a history of heart failure was taken to the cardiac catheterization lab. The cardiologist wanted to insert a device called a Swan-Ganz catheter into the right side of his heart to take different pressure measurements. The patient had been having symptoms associated with heart failure. His ability to pump blood from his heart was significantly impaired. He had accumulation of fluid in his lungs and his lower extremities. In fact, if you applied pressure on his legs with your thumb, you would make an indentation, similar to squeezing Play-Doh. He'd had a Swan-Ganz catheter placed in the past and unfortunately there was a complication. The anesthesia team had to be called to intubate him while the procedure was going on because of life-threating respiratory distress. This go-round, the decision was made to intubate the patient prior to the procedure.

The patient's intubation and cardiac catheterization went smoothly without complications. The pressures in his heart chambers and pulmonary arteries were concerning, however unchanged compared to prior readings. The decision was made to keep him intubated until the morning when the hospital was fully staffed just in case there was a problem during extubation. I studied the patient from head to toe. I reviewed his history and performed a physical exam. I ensured he was on the correct medications and that the proper labs were ordered for review on morning rounds. I also ordered an electrocardiogram, which was standard for all cardiac patients in intensive care. The patient's evening was uneventful.

The morning came and the critical care team huddled around the patient's room. I gathered my notes and prepared to present the case to the attending. He stood in front of the computer peering at the patient's electronic medical record. I was reviewing the case in my head when my thought process was interrupted.

"You know, Aerik, you should leave this hospital with your head down today," said the attending. He had an aggressive posture. His arms were folded. He had prominent wrinkles when he scowled. "You didn't put this patient on a beta-blocker. What is the literature on beta-blockers in the setting of heart failure?" He shook his head in disappointment.

A beta-blocker is a medication that slows the heart rate and is indicated in the management of heart failure. The reduction in heart rate decreases the heart tissue's energy demands. This is a concept that we learn early in medical school. Only a novice would make such a mistake. I was almost certain that I had started the patient on metoprolol, which is a type of beta-blocker. Everyone's eyes were fixated on me. The nurses, medical students, junior resident, and cardiology fellow were all staring at me. It was embarrassing. How could I have forgotten this?

I was preparing my response when the attending spoke. "Oh, never mind," he said flippantly. "I see it right here. You started him on metoprolol." He didn't say good morning. He didn't thank me for covering his unit overnight. He went straight to pimping my ass over a perceived mistake. He made an assumption and had full intent to embarrass me in front of my colleagues, not for the purpose of education, but for the purpose of ridicule. I was not surprised given his racist behavior only two years prior. He was singling me out. I had never heard him speak in such terms to other residents. Leave the hospital with my head down? He didn't apologize. Instead, he said it again.

"You know, Aerik, you should leave this hospital with your head down today. You didn't put this patient on a nitrate."

Now I was pissed because I knew I had started the patient on a nitroglycerin drip. In fact, I was staring at the nitroglycerin infusing through his intravenous line when the attending made the remark. I waited for him to find the medication listed in the medical record.

"Oh, never mind," he said. "I see you started him on a nitroglycerin drip." Again, there was no apology. He had me on the edge. You think he would have stopped. You think something would have triggered in his brain that I was competent and he should stop making assumptions. But he didn't. He continued to humiliate me.

"Aerik, you should leave this hospital with your head down," he said for a third time. "You didn't put this patient on tube feeds," he said again with disappointment.

He was correct. I didn't put the patient on tube feeds overnight. Tube feed is a nutritional supplement that flows from an external can through a nasogastric tube and down into the patient's stomach. It's vital nutrition for patients that are intubated and unable to ingest foods on their own. With that being said, the patient would only be intubated and sedated for twelve hours overnight. Do you get nutrition while you're sleeping? Now if the patient were to be intubated for several days, then surely I would have given more consideration to nutrition. Tube feeds for a twelve-hour period was his policy, which no other attending in the hospital followed.

The pimping session was not fruitful nor educational. It had a self-serving purpose…to humiliate. Certainly, he knows it's appropriate to first ensure that a medication wasn't ordered before ridiculing a resident. I had never seen him demonstrate similar behavior towards the other residents. I was pissed and there was nothing I could do about it.

Over the years, I've thought long and hard about the implications of malignant pimping. I've seen a few medical trainees have breakdowns similar to the aforementioned law student. The humiliation and anxiety can be difficult to compartmentalize. During the pimping, you can try to focus on what's substantial. You can try to focus on the educational point the attending is making. But at times, this is impossible. We are all human, and despite the strongest sense of self-worth, a superior telling you to leave the hospital with your head down in front of your peers, after a sleepless night of work, can be demoralizing. This can be very dangerous for the medicine trainee.

Where I trained, the residents purchased a bright, full spectrum light and put it in our lounge in order to increase production of the "happy" hormone called serotonin. As I detailed earlier, death and morbidity surround us. The schedule is taxing and we are sleep deprived. Our minds are distracted from the pleasures of this world and the things that enriched our lives prior to starting down the path of becoming a doctor. If you're not careful, you can find yourself in a chronic state of anhedonia. It can take some trainees only a small jolt to push them over the edge.

Arjun

When I was in medical school, I had a good buddy named Arjun. He was a tall, skinny Indian guy. He was clean-cut, with every hair on his head meticulously manicured. He was smart as hell, and by all accounts, very attractive. Arjun was part of our Buckeye Nuthouse crew and entrusted to perform the most vital of duties. When we arrived at the bar, we would send him out for reconnaissance. He would make his way through the crowds until he found a group of unoccupied ladies. He would draw them in with his soft mannerisms and then send us the signal.

Arjun was one of the good guys. He loved medicine because he loved people. He loved their stories. He told me once that his favorite part of the patient encounter was asking people what makes them happy. He adored grandparents talking about their grandchildren and young people that were passionate about their jobs. On the occasion where a patient would mention an activity with which he was unfamiliar, he would ask them to explain. His patients from rural Ohio taught him about hunting and fishing. Though he had no affinity for these activities, he was satisfied living vicariously through the patient's joy, even if only for a moment.

Arjun loved studying neurology and he processed these concepts faster than most medical students. He could localize the anatomic region of a stroke based on symptoms without the aid of a CT scan. Neurology was challenging to me. I had to memorize the different synapses and neurotransmitters, and frequently confused the parasympathetic and sympathetic nervous systems. When asked questions by my attending, my answers seemed jagged and forced. Arjun's answers were smooth and confident. He possessed an innate gift and was a giant step ahead of his peers.

Arjun changed during his fourth year of medical school. He always looked tired and ragged. His once pleasant conversations became terse. He seemed so irritable. I saw him in the cafeteria one afternoon and tapped him on his shoulder.

"What's up, man? Wanna sit together?" I asked him.

"No, man. I'm good. Gotta run," he said, barely making eye contact. I could tell he was lying.

"You sure? Just take a few minutes. A quick bite?"

"Okay. Just for a minute though," he said. We found a table far away from the masses. He sat slouched in his chair, running his fork through some vegetables. He broke the silence. "I heard about what the urology attending said to you."

"Yup," I chuckled. A few weeks prior, the urology attending told me blacks have head structures that may make it difficult for us to learn. "He's an asshole," I said.

"It's not funny, man. Why are you smiling?" His demeanor turned in an instant. His face was boiling red and he was gripping the hell out of his fork. I noticed the blue bags underneath his eyes and the wrinkles at his brow. He looked exhausted.

"Chill out, man," I said. "I know it's not funny. I'm chuckling because I can't believe he had the audacity to say that shit. The guy is an equal opportunity bigot. He says the same shit to women, Mormons, Asians. He's just trying to get a rise out of us."

"But why does he get away with it?" Arjun was now yelling. A few employees glanced at our table. "That's not right," he said with a softer tone.

"I know it's not right."

"Well, then why didn't you report him?" Arjun asked.

"He's been reported before and nothing happens. Plus I'm not that type. He better hope I don't see his ass on High Street though."

"This stuff is pissing me off." Arjun was again climaxing to a rage. "How can people treat others like this and get away with it?" We sat in silence for a few seconds before he continued. "My resident and I were called to see a stroke patient last week. We did everything correct. We gave all the right medicine, ordered all the right imaging, and contacted all the right people. I was actually feeling proud of myself. This morning an attending approached us on rounds and said, 'You know that patient died.' I thought we were about to have a productive conversation. Nope! He just started yelling at our asses. He told us we didn't recognize the stroke early enough. He questioned our medical acumen in the middle of the fucking hallway. There were patients walking by, for Christ's sake." The entire cafeteria was looking at us. "I think I know what a stroke looks like. The shit he was saying made no sense. I ran the case by another attending and I was told we did everything appropriately. I was also told that some attendings are in the habit of just being assholes." He threw his fork into his mashed potatoes and was shaking his head with frustration. "I gotta go, man. I've got to get to rounds."

"Hey, man. You need some help?" I asked. I was very concerned about Arjun.

"How can you help me? How can I get well while working in the system that is making me sick?"

Arjun left lunch clearly angered. He was no longer the soft-spoken guy that loved people. He hated the process, and it had changed him. He committed suicide during his intern year.

According to a study published in *Academic Medicine*[4], the second most common cause of death amongst training medical residents from 2000 through 2014 was suicide (66 suicides of 311 deaths). The study found that residents aged 35–44 and 45–54 had suicide rates that exceeded their respective cohorts. In a 2016 study compiling data from over 100,000 medical students, 27 percent experienced depressive symptoms and 11 percent had thoughts of suicide.[5] In May 2018, renewed interest in this topic was spurred when a New York University medical student and a New York University psychiatry resident died by suicide only five days apart from each other.

Pamela Wible is a physician who has studied and published articles on physician suicide. She has developed a registry that tallies 949 physician suicide deaths by May 2018. The list is ever growing. She was able to discuss the New York University suicides with people close to the deceased. She spoke with an individual who apparently has intimate knowledge of the culture of the New York University Hospital. Their interview is published online.[6] The source states, "There are posters offering counseling services and heartfelt emails being sent to the students, but here's one thing no one in power to help is mentioning—the supervisors and their bullying." The source describes the bullying as a cancer. In a very powerful statement, the source is quoted as follows: "If we look at these people who are fueling these toxic work environments, who are bullying and intimidating others, what they most need is to be taken out of the situation not only for those they serve but for themselves because it is something that will create disease and disruption in themselves as well. It needs to stop."

There is no room on the medical wards, or in our society for that matter, for malignant ridicule. It is not inconsequential. It needs to stop.

Wrong Number

A few years ago, I had a conversation with a colleague who was an Internal Medicine chief resident. Chief residents are selected by the Internal Medicine faculty. These individuals typically stand out from their resident peers. In her case, it's very easy to see why she was chosen. She was a very smart woman who eventually became a cardiologist. She embodies the spirit of the Hippocratic oath. She is perhaps the most compassionate physician that I have ever met.

As a chief resident, you take home call in the evenings and are spared sleeping in the hospital beds overnight. If a resident needs the opinion of a more seasoned physician, they may reach out to the chief resident. It's very rare that a chief will receive a page, but it can happen as detailed in the following story that was described by my colleague.

A patient was admitted to the hospital in a precarious condition. The patient had end-stage liver disease and death was imminent. The family was told that the patient may not make it through the night. The patient made the decision not to be resuscitated in the event of his death. The chronic and pernicious nature of his disease state meant that even if he was resuscitated, he would very soon succumb to his illness. The day team of residents that admitted the patient would not be staying in the hospital overnight. Instead, a night team of residents would be taking over his care. Instructions were clearly passed between the day admitting residents and the night residents. Continuity of care is disturbed in this model. Ideally, at least one person from the admitting team would be in the hospital at all times, as they were most familiar with this case; however, ACGME restrictions have led to the creation of multiple teams in the hospital and hence, multiple patient handoffs.

In the early a.m. hours, the night resident received a page from the nursing staff. Unfortunately, the patient's blood pressure was dropping and in a matter of minutes he would succumb to his disease. The night resident reviewed her notes and realized the patient was not to be resuscitated in the event of his death. She arrived at the patient room and confirmed what had been relayed by the nursing staff. She reviewed the patient chart and retrieved the phone number for the family contact. She dialed the number and woke a family member from their sleep. The family member was hysterically crying. She inquired what had happened. How did their loved one pass? They had just seen him only a few hours ago. They were devastated. This is a strange reaction considering they were just told that death was imminent.

The night resident went through the formalities of documenting death. She did a physical exam and noted the absence of heart sounds and the absence of air moving in and out of the lungs. There was a flat line on telemetry. She opened the patient's eyelids and shined a light directly at the pupils. They did not constrict. She pronounced the patient dead, wrote a note in the patient chart, and filled out all necessary paperwork. The patient remained in the room until the hospital staff would be able to secure his body and take him to the morgue. The resident left the floor to attend to her other duties. It was routine, one of several deaths she would witness in her career as a trainee.

The family drove to the hospital in the early morning hours and made their way to the patient room. They were wailing and overcome with grief. There was a sense of disbelief. How had he died? He was fine just a few hours ago. They went into the room to say their goodbyes prior to him being taken to the morgue. In his room they encountered a warm body. The telemetry machine was turned on and it displayed a normal blood pressure and heart rhythm. The television was on just as it had been when they left him that evening. To the family's pleasant surprise, their crying awoke their loved one.

When contacting the family, the resident had opened the wrong chart and dialed the wrong number. The chief resident had to be called.

I've witnessed many mistakes in medicine. I've made several boneheaded mistakes myself. But I can honestly say I've never seen or heard of anything like this. I felt terrible for the family but also for the resident. She had made an error. I'm sure she was exhausted. Her body and her mind were rotating between functioning during days and nights. She's obviously an intelligent woman. She was able to secure a spot in medical school and at a top-tier medicine residency. She simply made a mistake. Surprise ... she's human.

I asked the chief resident how she responded after she was paged about the incident. The chief didn't chastise her. She didn't ridicule her. She didn't offer the resident a dime to call her mother. What good would that do? It was over. The resident had suffered enough. The chief stressed the importance of reviewing the patient chart before calling a family member. Her response was educational. I assure you, the resident will double-check phone numbers until the day she retires.

CHAPTER 3

Unaffordable Health Care

Refusal to Pay

The final year of medical school was a breeze. After three years of intensive study, it's hard not to have senioritis. My grades were determined, and my licensing exams were complete. I had submitted my residency applications in the early fall, and it was time to relax. I filled my schedule with electives that required the least number of hours possible in the hospital. I was renewed with the simple pleasures of life. I ate my meals on time, I wasn't forced to hold my bladder until the end of Medicine rounds, and I got at least eight hours of sleep with the occasional midday nap. I was back in the gymnasium lifting weights and focusing on physical fitness. I skipped out on a few medical student lectures and even made the gutsy call to skip a day in the operating room while on my Anesthesia rotation to head up to Ann Arbor for the annual Ohio State versus Michigan football game. It was a well-deserved respite.

Now, I was warned by seasoned physicians not to take this route. They advised that I keep myself attuned to all aspects of medicine. When you stop engaging yourself in the craft of medicine, concepts will start to seep out of your brain. I understood their intentions and I agreed. But I was exhausted and so were all the other fourth-year medical students; therefore, most of us took the easy road. We enjoyed our family and friends during our final year of medical school. It was our last chance to rest before the start of internship.

Turns out the senior physicians were correct. A few months before graduation, an uneasy feeling crept into my belly. Very soon I would have a medical doctorate and be in charge of managing patients. The confidence that I had gained during my third year of medical school had dissipated faster than the beers we drank at dollar beer night. It was difficult to be excited about medical school graduation when the responsibility of internship was staring me straight in the face. I would be moving to Philadelphia to start my career as a physician at Thomas Jefferson University. I eased my fears by convincing myself that I would start on an easy rotation, likely in the outpatient setting. That would allow me to ramp up my studying and get back into the mind-set of medicine. To my dismay, I opened an email from the Thomas Jefferson University chief residents a few weeks before commencement.

I was to start in the medical intensive care unit (MICU). This is where the sickest of all patients are treated. The ICU mortality rate is 11.3 percent.[7] ICU patients have multiple organs affected by disease, making their management very complicated. An understanding of every facet of medicine is critical in managing patients in the ICU. I was starting to regret skipping out on my fourth-year ICU elective.

I started my internship and it took me a few days to get into the groove, but boy was it fun once I found it. It was mentally taxing and physically challenging. I worked twelve-hour shifts three days in a row, followed by a thirty-hour shift, often without any sleep. I saw so much pathology it made my head spin. We resuscitated patients with CPR almost daily. I became adept at managing sepsis. I even started performing procedures such as lumbar punctures with minimal help from the senior residents. That month went by in a flash, but the memories stick with me to this day.

I remember very fondly a patient named Ms. Garcia. She was a petite African American woman in her sixties who was heavily involved in Philadelphia politics. Approximately six months prior to our introduction, she noticed a mass growing in her abdomen. The mass was small, the size of a marble at most. She paid it no attention and continued her days trying to grow support for the Republican party. As the days went on, she noticed that the mass was slowly growing. It grew to the size of a golf ball. Weeks later it grew to the size of a tennis ball. Weeks later it grew to the size of a softball. Weeks later it grew to the size of a basketball. It was only then that Ms. Garcia, at the urging of her family, decided to see a doctor. The mass was causing significant abdominal pain. She had lost about thirty pounds since the onset of symptoms. A CT scan revealed a heterogenous mass concerning for cancer. It also showed that the mass was obstructing one of her kidneys close to the ureter. The ureter drains urine from the kidney into the bladder. If the ureter is obstructed, fluid can build up in the kidney, causing excruciating pain. The decision was made to fix the kidney and ureter problem prior to biopsy of the mass, which is crucial for the definitive diagnosis of cancer.

Ms. Garcia arrived to the interventional radiology suite one morning. The physicians prepped her flank with alcohol and iodine in order to prevent infection. Once the kidney was identified using ultrasonography, the physician injected local anesthetic into the skin to minimize pain. An 18-gauge needle pierced the skin and was carefully guided into an open space within the pelvis of the kidney. The physicians then guided a wire through the needle, until it nestled perfectly into position. The final step was to guide a catheter over the wire so that her kidney would drain fluid externally through the catheter and bypass the obstructing mass. The catheter was sewn into place, and cloudy, yellow urine drained into a container. The procedure was going smoothly until things went devastatingly wrong.

Ms. Garcia suddenly complained of shortness of breath. She began panting and pointing to her chest. Her oxygen saturation began to drop and her heart rate increased steadily. Then, in an instant, she went unconscious. It happened that quickly. She was no longer with us.

"Code Blue, Interventional Radiology." The overhead speaker was blaring. Suddenly a team of physicians and nurses surrounded Ms. Garcia. There was a flat line on the telemetry machine. The senior resident began pumping on her chest. It became chaotic inside the radiology suite. Nurses and physicians had defined roles but were bumping into each other at a frenetic pace. Multiple loud conversations were going on at the same time, each of which was vital to patient management. It's difficult to explain, but within that chaos was a degree of organization.

"One milligram of epinephrine!" the senior resident demanded. "Get a central line kit!" A central line was placed into her femoral vein to deliver the epinephrine. He continued to pound on her chest. The respiratory team grabbed a breathing device called an ambu bag and delivered oxygen into her lungs. A junior resident reviewed her chart.

"Likely a pulmonary embolism," the junior resident said with a sense of calm. He was the only one in the room that seemed stoic, concentrating on the details of the recorded physician notes. "She has a cancerous mass in her abdomen." Cancer does put patients in a physiologic state that increases the chance of developing blood clots. These clots can lodge into the pulmonary arteries and, if large enough, lead to cardiac arrest. A sudden increase in heart rate and a sudden decrease in oxygen saturation in a patient with cancer is highly suspicious for a clot that has migrated to the lungs.

"Another milligram of epinephrine," the senior resident yelled as he continued to pound on her chest. This routine continued for twenty minutes, epinephrine and chest compressions, epinephrine and chest compressions. There was no change in Ms. Garcia's status. She just lay there, without any voluntary movement. As the time elapsed, the chance of survival diminished. It was up to the senior resident when to call the code to completion. He had the discretion to discontinue life-saving measures, and he was very close. His arms were tired from pumping on Ms. Garcia's chest. There was a stillness in the room. The staff had lost their energy. There was no longer any chaos. They were all awaiting the instruction to stop the CPR protocol. They had given Ms. Garcia everything they had. Her chance for survival had plummeted.

"She's in ventricular fibrillation!" the junior resident yelled. He noticed the change in her heart rhythm in between chest compressions. "Shock her!" The pads had already been placed on her chest in the case that defibrillation ("shocking") was necessary. A jolt was delivered, and with that, her heart returned to a normal rhythm.

The good news was that Ms. Garcia didn't die. The bad news was that Ms. Garcia remained unconscious, and a CT scan of her chest did in fact reveal a pulmonary embolism. She had gone a few minutes without oxygen delivery to vital organs, including her brain. Her prognosis was poor at best.

She was taken to the ICU immediately after the code. The anesthesia team performed intubation and hooked her up to a ventilator machine. She was sedated with intravenous propofol and started on heparin in order to prevent any new blood clots from forming.

As I stated prior, the problem with ICU patients is that there typically isn't just one insult to the body. Ms. Garcia, for example, had a pulmonary embolism lodged into her lungs. In addition, she had a cancerous mass that was obstructing her urinary system. It turns out the cloudy urine that I previously mentioned was infected. A urine culture showed a bug called E. coli. Unfortunately, the bug migrated to her blood, a condition called urosepsis, which caused her blood pressure to drop significantly. The urosepsis led to kidney impairment, therefore she was no longer able to excrete toxic metabolites from her body. She had to be placed on dialysis. The body works in sequence and perfect harmony. Insult to one organ can lead to desynchrony and have deleterious effects on other organ systems. Approximately two weeks into her ICU stay, Ms. Garcia remained intubated and sedated without much improvement in her health. During morning rounds, the attending critical care physician gave a grave prognosis to the family.

The family, however, was resolute. They flooded the hospital in numbers that were too many to count. They held hands around her hospital bed and prayed for a miracle. There was someone by her bedside at all times, even in the early morning hours. They refused to give up. I sided with science. I believe in God, but I also believe in empirical evidence. One does not preclude the other. Just like many other patients I cared for in the ICU that month, she was going to die.

The events that occurred over the next week taught me a lesson that I've kept to this day. Though it is my job to give patients empirical data about their prognosis, I should not speak in definitive terms. Ultimately, I'm not in control. Ms. Garcia's health began to turn the corner. The infection in her blood cleared with antibiotics. The medicines used to keep her blood pressure at normal levels were no longer needed. Streaks of urine began to flow from the tube that was placed in the interventional radiology suite only a few weeks prior, a sign that her kidneys were starting to work. It also became evident that she was becoming less reliant on the ventilator machine. "Praise God!" a family member announced once given the news.

I'll never forget the morning I arrived in Ms. Garcia's room after she was extubated, able to finally breathe on her own. She looked exhausted, not uncommon for a patient on propofol sedation for three weeks. Her silver hair was disheveled. She flickered her eyes while adjusting to her first sunlight in almost one month. Each movement appeared to be slow and calculated. She turned her head to the door as I entered her patient room. "Good morning, Ms. Garcia. It's a pleasure to see you awake." She continued to turn her head until her eyes fixed on my figure.

"Young man," she said, pointing her finger at me with a bit of a tremor. She was hoarse and barely audible, a consequence of a prolonged state of intubation. "Young man!" she repeated with a little more fortitude.

"Yes, ma'am."

"Come here," she said in a whisper.

I took a few steps closer. "I'm very pleased that you are talking. You have come a long way."

She put her index finger over her lips, a gesture that indicated I should stop talking. "Come closer," she whispered.

I took another step closer. "Yes, ma'am. What can I do for you?"

"You can come closer," she said. I took another step and was now pressed against the arm of her hospital bed. I thought she wanted to hug me out of gratitude. "Closer," she said. I leaned in. Our cheeks almost touched. Perhaps she wanted a kiss? "Can you hear me?" she asked.

"Yes, ma'am. I can hear you," I said, waiting for her to embrace me.

"Good. You are listening then," she said. "I want you to know that I'm not paying for any of this!" She then slowly turned her atrophied neck muscles towards the window and away from me.

She was nearly dead three weeks ago. The sepsis could have killed her. The pulmonary embolism could have killed her. The kidney failure could have killed her. We literally pounded on her chest for twenty minutes to keep her alive after she avoided doctors for months while a mass the size of a basketball grew in her abdomen. Her primary concern after being comatose for three weeks was not her cancer prognosis, but rather the cost of her hospitalization. She had more concern for her bank account than her organs.

Health-Care Costs

The things we can do in the operating rooms, hospital floors, and medical clinics in the United States of America are truly amazing. Molecular testing can identify genes that are overactive in cancer patients, allowing us to give more targeted therapy. Urologists can use a robot to remove a prostate. Allergists are desensitizing kids with peanut allergies so that they are able to tolerate a full peanut butter and jelly sandwich without as much as a hive. The University of Miami developed a protocol to implant insulin-producing islet cells into patients with diabetes, rendering them no longer dependent on insulin. These medical miracles are continuous and evolving.

As one would expect, such advancement is not cheap. The 2018 estimated federal budget for research and development at the National Institutes of Health was $37 billion and the clinical and translational science funding budget was $543 million.[8] Note that this is representative of federal dollars only. Pharmaceutical companies and others in the biotechnology world will spend big bucks too.

Medical research, hospital services, ambulatory services, home health care, medical insurance, prescription drugs, etc.

cost our country $3.5 trillion in 2017.[9] The public is left to pay this health-care bill. This steep cost has created much scrutiny and political divide. Many point to the cost of health care in countries with similar wealth. In 2016, the average dollars spent on health care per person in comparable wealth countries was $4,908.[10] The average dollars spent per person in the United States that same year was $10,348, over twice as much![10] The rate of health-care spending as a percent of GDP in the United States has increased at a faster rate than in comparable countries. In 2016, we spent nearly 18 percent of our GDP on health care, more than any other country. Switzerland came in second at 13 percent.[10]

This higher cost could be considered palatable if health-care outcomes in the United States were favorable compared to countries of similar wealth. Certainly, you wouldn't purchase a luxury car just because it costs more. A higher cost would mandate better safety outcomes, better fuel efficiency, up-to-date navigation systems, etc.

In a study published in the *Journal of the American Medical Association*, lead investigator Irene Papanicolas compared health-care outcomes amongst eleven high-income countries. She found that the United States had the lowest life expectancy and highest infant mortality rate.[11] Data from the Kaiser Family Foundation demonstrates that hospital admission for preventable diseases including asthma, congestive heart failure, and diabetes is higher in the United States than in comparable countries.[12] The European Observatory on Health Systems and Policies found that in 2013 more people died in the United States from preventable diseases or their complications than those in twelve other high-income countries.

So, are our costs justified, or does Ms. Garcia have a point?

Big Pharma Sets the Price

In full disclosure, in the past I have spoken for Mylan, a pharmaceutical company. This name may sound familiar. Mylan acquired the EpiPen* in 2007. EpiPen is indicated for patients who have a history of a severe allergic reaction to allergens such as insect venom or a food such as peanuts. The EpiPen is an autoinjector that delivers epinephrine rapidly, which is vital in the setting of a severe allergic reaction. Retrospective data has shown that epinephrine can save lives by abating an allergic inflammatory response. Therefore, the Allergy Joint Task Force Guidelines recommend that every patient at risk for anaphylaxis be prescribed an epinephrine autoinjector. The EpiPen is one of several epinephrine autoinjectors on the market.

The EpiPen cost the patient about $57 when Mylan acquired it. Mylan marketed this drug aggressively and dominated the epinephrine autoinjector market. In fact, most people refer to all epinephrine autoinjectors as "EpiPen," despite the fact that there are multiple other autoinjectors available. Mylan received an unexpected gift in 2015 when their chief competitor, Auvi-Q, discontinued production. As Mylan gained a stranglehold on the market, the price of

EpiPen steadily increased. In 2013, the price was approximately $265, and in 2015, the price was approximately $461. In 2016, the price suddenly jumped to $609! According to one source, the cost to Mylan per device was only $35![13] That's a pretty good profit margin. Now consider there were 3.6 million Americans prescribed an EpiPen in 2015, some of which were prescribed multiple devices![14]

As you can imagine, the rising cost of the EpiPen didn't sit well with the public. An indelible image from the *New York Times* in June of 2017 depicts an EpiPen piñata being smacked with a rod.[15] Hundreds of gold coins are spewing from the piñata and onto the floor. During this time period, there was an influx of patients coming into my allergy clinic, ticked off that they had to cut down on back-to-school spending so that their child had access to lifesaving epinephrine.

With all of this being said, it didn't take me long to say yes after I was asked to be a speaker. I didn't agree to a Mylan contract because of speaker reimbursement. In fact, my reimbursement from Mylan was a small fraction of my salary. To be honest, my preference on the evenings of my EpiPen presentations was to be home playing basketball with my son. After a full day of work, the last thing I wanted to do was public speaking. I agreed because I needed to educate the community on the use of epinephrine. There are forty to fifty deaths in the United States every year from venom sting reactions. Many of these deaths could have been avoided if the deceased had access to an epinephrine autoinjector. In Rowan

County, where my office is located, we have had at least two deaths in the past four years from venom sting allergy. I also came to find that many practitioners were unclear as to when to prescribe an epinephrine autoinjector. I saw speaking for Mylan's EpiPen product as an opportunity to educate. I was just as appalled with the price increase as the public. When I was asked the difficult questions regarding cost, which inevitably arose with each presentation, I passed those questions over to the sales representative who was also in attendance. Her response was always truthful but insufficient and without explanation. "Yes, the cost of our product has increased; however, we do offer discount cards that *may* reduce the cost for patients with commercial insurance." The audience was always unsatisfied with her answer, but what did they expect her to say, "Mylan increased the price of the EpiPen in the name of corporate greed"?

I did also sign on to speak for another pharmaceutical company named Teva for a product called Cinqair*. Cinqair is a medicine that works well in patients with uncontrolled and severe asthma with a predominance of a white blood cell called an eosinophil. Many patients that are candidates for this drug are dependent on high-dose systemic steroids to control their asthma. High-dose systemic steroids are associated with side effects such as adrenal insufficiency, osteoporosis, avascular necrosis, etc. These are not insignificant side effects.

I've seen miraculous improvement in asthma symptoms in patients started on Cinqair. I've seen a grandfather able to play basketball with his grandchildren for the first time without wheezing and a mom who was able to walk down the supermarket aisle without stopping to catch her breath. Equally as important, many Cinqair patients are able to stop their systemic steroids, which alleviates the concern of the aforementioned side effects. This drug should be introduced to all physicians that manage asthma because of its effect on a patient's quality of life; therefore, I was very happy to represent the drug.

Cinqair, however, is disadvantageous because of its method of delivery. Cinqair is administered intravenously, which means a nurse must stick a patient's vein with a needle every month for an infusion. This is an onerous task, but some patients are willing to suffer the discomfort so that they are able to live without respiratory symptoms.

There are two other drugs in the same class as Cinqair that have similar mechanisms of action and similar efficacy; however, these drugs separate themselves because they are administered by subcutaneous injection instead of intravenous infusion. Who would sign up for monthly intravenous infusions when subcutaneous injection products are available? I would rather stick a needle in the subcutaneous fat of my belly than stick a needle into my vein. In addition, Cinqair intravenous infusions can take several minutes. A subcutaneous injection is finished within seconds.

At the time of my training to speak for Cinqair, the Teva team was developing a subcutaneous product that would be competitive in the marketplace. Unfortunately, the subcutaneous form of Cinqair never made it to the market, likely because it was not as efficacious as expected. I made the decision that I would use intravenous Cinqair sparingly and rely heavily on the other two drugs in the same class, which have similar clinical efficacy but are delivered subcutaneously. My decision was solely based on patient comfort. As the number of my Cinqair prescriptions reduced, the less I saw of the Teva representatives. I was never put on a schedule to speak for the drug. I certainly could have ingratiated myself to Teva and prescribed Cinqair despite its less desirable route of intravenous administration, but I would have been doing my patients a disservice.

Teva found me to be an expert in the field of asthma, hence the original invitation to be a speaker. When the subcutaneous version of the drug failed to come to fruition and I made the patient-minded decision to prescribe the competitor products, I was no longer of value to Teva. Certainly I would be asked during a presentation my personal thoughts on Cinqair and I would have to state that there are other products on the market that are more easily administered. It's apparent that Teva and I have different goals. I'm interested in educating the physicians in my county about a class of drugs that has been shown to reduce asthma flares and systemic steroid use. My main goal is physician education. In my opinion, Teva's main goal is to sell their product. They too are interested in physician education and reducing asthma flares, however, only in conjunction with their product.

This is capitalism in its purest form. Now don't get me wrong, I have no problems with capitalism and I have no problems with a for-profit operation. I have no problems with Teva not putting me on a speaker schedule. Why would Teva want a speaker who prescribes competitor products?

The problem with Big Pharma is not capitalism. The problem lies in the constructs in which Teva, Mylan, and other pharmaceutical companies operate. It is within these constructs that pharmaceutical companies are allowed to reap big profits while crippling the health-care market. Health care is not a true market. If you were prescribed Cinqair, you would likely have no idea that there are competitor drugs on the market. How would you know? There's no Kelley Blue Book or Zillow for this class of medicine. You would consider alternatives if you were buying a car or a house. Why aren't you considering alternatives when purchasing a medicine?

In the current health-care construct, the power oftentimes lies in the hands of a third party, such as a pharmaceutical company. They set the price. When a patient asks me how much Cinqair is going to cost, I shrug my shoulders. I'm not privy to any arrangement that Teva has made with a patient's insurance company. I truly have no idea how much the drug is going to cost them. That's a problem. In a true market, the power lies more with the consumer. The consumer is able to understand the alternative choices and the associated cost. This allows for a fair market price, instead of a price that is determined solely by Pharma.

What can happen when Pharma sets the price? Do you remember Martin Shkreli? As the CEO of Turing Pharmaceuticals, he obtained the manufacturing license for a drug call Daraprim, which can be lifesaving in patients with certain immunodeficiencies. In 2015, he raised the price of this drug by 5,000 percent, from $13.50 per pill to $750 per pill! This led to a congressional hearing, but no charges. It's not illegal. The current construct is set so that Pharma sets the price for Daraprim, EpiPen, Cinqair, etc., and it seems as if there is nothing that anyone can do about it.

"Help a Sista Out"

I don't lose my temper too frequently in clinic. My nursing staff will attest to that. In fact, over my five years of private practice I've been irate only once. A representative from Sanofi, a France-based pharmaceutical company, came into my office one afternoon promoting the aforementioned epinephrine autoinjector called Auvi-Q, the direct competitor to EpiPen. She gave me several reasons why I should prescribe Auvi-Q over the competitor product. I told her that I had been very comfortable using EpiPen, and I didn't see my prescription habits changing. I also told her that 50 percent of my patients have government insurance, and since Auvi-Q isn't on government formularies, I wouldn't be using her drug. She proceeded to tell me that I do see 33 percent nongovernment Blue Cross Blue Shield patients. I'm not sure how she gathered that data, but she was correct. She asked me to guarantee her that I would prescribe Auvi-Q to all of my Blue Cross Blue Shield patients that required an epinephrine autoinjector. I told her that I couldn't make such a guarantee, to which she responded, "Help a sista out, Dr. Williams!"

I guess she was under the assumption that because we were both black, I would give preference to her product. As I said prior, the main goal of Big Pharma is to sell their product. I asked her to leave my office. I had planned on calling her supervisors to alert them that their representative would no longer be allowed to call on my clinic, but this was a moot point. Sanofi voluntarily pulled their product off the market shortly thereafter amid concerns that the autoinjector device delivered an inaccurate dose of epinephrine.

In 2017, the product was reintroduced to the market by a pharmaceutical company named Kaléo. Its reintroduction was welcomed given the increase in price of EpiPen and the outrage that ensued. Physicians and patients were eager to see if Kaléo would provide a more price-conscious product. On the surface, Kaléo came through. The charge to the patient who had commercial insurance was $0! Patients were ecstatic. The news traveled quickly and I started receiving daily phone calls from patients about prescribing the product. I thought the whole thing sounded too good to be true. My skepticism led to some research. I found that the charge to the consumer who had commercial insurance was indeed $0; however, the list price was approximately $4,500, more than seven times the list price for EpiPen! Kaléo has set that price. Kaléo knows only a small percentage of insurers will reimburse for this list price, but that's all they need, just a few. If your insurance does not cover Auvi-Q, you will receive the product for "free." One can reasonably infer that the few insurers that pay for Auvi-Q will make up that difference. What a brilliant strategy.

Shortly after the announcement of Auvi-Q returning to the market, their pharmaceutical representative came into my office. He was ecstatic about the product and I shared in his excitement. The product itself is sleek. The device has an automated voice that walks the patient through the epinephrine injection sequence step-by-step. In addition, the device is smaller than a cell phone and can fit in a patient's pocket, which is an upgrade from the bulky EpiPen device.

"So how much does it cost?" I asked.

"It's zero dollars for commercial patients," he said.

The conversation was cordial until this point. "Free?" I asked.

"That's right, Dr. Williams. It's zero dollars for commercial patients."

"That's bullshit!" I yelled. "It costs $4,500!" I heard my practice manager walk towards my office. She peeked her head in, surprised to hear me use profanity. They still jab at me on occasion about the time I cussed at a pharmaceutical representative.

Why was I so angry? I work in Salisbury, North Carolina. It's a rural town about forty miles northeast of Charlotte, with a population of about 35,000 people. Salisbury is the home of the Cheerwine soft drink, the National Sportscasters and Sportswriters Association, and Food Lion supermarket. The people of Salisbury take pride in their town. They rally around their girls softball team, which went to the world series in 2017 for the third straight year. More than 30,000 people packed the streets for a festival commemorating the one-hundred-year anniversary of Cheerwine in 2017, and the house is always full at the Piedmont Players Theatre productions. There is a sense of community in Salisbury. People smile and wave though they've never met.

It is not an affluent city. Salisbury's per capita income is just over $24,000.[16] According to Data USA, 22.9 percent of the city's population lives below the poverty line, which is higher than the national average (14 percent).[17] Medicaid comprises 35 percent of my patient population.

Salisbury has decent, hardworking people. Unfortunately, I've seen patients have to make the difficult decision between buying their child's medication or buying school clothes. This is not an exaggeration. I have patients that will skip doses of their asthma medicine intentionally so that their inhaler will "last longer." They would rather wheeze so they can put dinner on the table.

Nothing is free. Kaléo knows that as well as I do. You may not see cost when your Auvi-Q is delivered to your house, but it does add to the health-care bill. Believe you me, somebody is paying the $4,500 for the Auvi-Q. It may seem as if no money comes from your pocket when the device is delivered at your door, but it does. The insurer must make up that cost. So they increase your insurance premium, your specialist co-payment, your deductible, your out-of-pocket maximum payment, etc. These seem to rise annually. Unfortunately, this rising cost means that our poorest must decide between buying medications and basic necessities.

Little is known about how Big Pharma sets the list price of their drugs. We do know that the prices are high and the reward is big. We also know that the US spends about $370 billion per year on pharmaceuticals, which is about 17 percent of all health-care spending. This is more than any other high-income country.[18] We know this is reflected in our rising insurance premiums, co-payments at doctor visits, insurance deductibles, and out-of-pocket maximum payments. What we also know is that of the forty-four health companies that made the Fortune 500 list in 2017, ten were pharmaceutical companies.[19] We also know that nine out of ten Big Pharma companies spend more money on marketing than on research and development.[20] Why? Because their main goal is to sell their product, and they're doing a damn good job.

Linear Patent Extension

Qvar is an asthma medication manufactured by Teva Pharmaceuticals. In prior years, it existed as a hydrofluoro-alkane (HFA) inhaler that sprays out medicine in the form of a mist. It's a fantastic medication. The particle size of the drug is small, allowing drug delivery deep into the smaller airways of the lungs. There are other medications in Qvar's class; however, I almost exclusively prescribe Qvar because of its efficacy and affordability. In 2017 a representative from Teva came into my office unannounced for a chat. She told me that Teva would be discontinuing Qvar in its current form as the mist inhaler. She explained that the company would still be manufacturing Qvar; however, the delivery mechanism had changed. Instead of using the HFA device, the medicine would be delivered through a device termed the "RediHaler." I asked her why the company had decided to make the change. She explained that the new RediHaler eliminates the need for hand-breath coordination while inhaling. The device also doesn't need to be primed or shaken before its use. She assured me that the cost of Qvar would not change.

That sounded interesting, but I wasn't convinced. I follow the asthma literature fairly closely, and I was unaware of any scientific evidence that demonstrated a new RediHaler improved drug delivery to the lungs. When I asked the representative for this data, she stated it didn't exist. So then why create a new device if it hasn't been shown to have some clinical benefit? I don't recall what the representative said next because I was no longer paying attention. I was racking my brain trying to figure out why Teva would make such a move … and then it clicked.

"Is this about a linear patent extension?" I interrupted while she was rambling. I could tell she was shocked that I asked. Most physicians probably wouldn't have made the connection. She nodded in the affirmative. In my opinion, the excuse for the switch was a cover for a linear extension.

When pharmaceutical companies formulate an idea, they must protect it, and that protection comes in the form of a patent. In the absence of a patent, a company can spend millions of dollars creating a new drug molecule only to have a competitor create a similar drug and share in their profit. This is obviously unfair. The process of obtaining a patent begins when the pharmaceutical company files an application with the United States Patent and Trademark Office. Once granted, the inventor has approximately twenty years of market exclusivity from the date of application. This may seem like a long time, but companies typically apply for the patent during the drug discovery phase, prior to performing studies showing drug efficacy and prior to the burdensome process of FDA approval. This may leave only half of the patent period for a pharmaceutical company to obtain a return on their investment. Once the patent period has ended, the doors open for generic products to enter the market, which causes a significant revenue drop for the company that developed the original drug. In a 2016 article titled "Patent Cliff and Strategic Switch: Exploring Strategic Design Possibilities in the Pharmaceutical Industry," the authors stated that they expect the "impending patent cliff" to erode greater than $100 billion in sales in the coming years.[21]

In order to delay the impending patent cliff, it appears incontrovertible to me that Teva made a change from the

HFA device to the RediHaler. I refuse to believe they had patient care in mind when making this change. The Teva representative stated there is no data to suggest that patients using a RediHaler have any better outcomes than those using the HFA inhaler. This simple adjustment in the device allows for Teva to obtain a patent extension and to remain on the market longer without competition from generics. What does that mean for asthma patients? Well, the cost hasn't changed, so they won't be charged more and they will continue to have access to Qvar. Unfortunately, it also means that cheaper generic products with the same efficacy will not be available until patent expiration, which has been prolonged by the linear extension. This allows Teva to continue to prosper with its Qvar product but costs the asthma patient the opportunity to buy generic. Once again, more expensive medicine leads to more expensive insurance premiums, co-payments, deductibles, and out-of-pocket maximum payments. I emphasize that this is not illegal. Teva is operating within the constructs of the health-care system, but this loophole does increase Ms. Garcia's insurance premium payment. Is this what we want?

Pharmaceutical companies can make other savvy moves to keep their product on the market for as long as possible without fear of generic competition. A tweak in the delivery system of an inhaler can buy more patent years as described above. "Pay for delay" agreements describe when a branded company pays a generic company not to launch a competitor drug to ensure further market time without competition. Generic drug companies need the branded drugs in order to test the generic drug's efficacy. Some branded companies are not willing to provide their product for testing. Their reluctance costs the federal government $3.8 billion over ten years because access would allow the development of cheaper generic drugs for Medicaid and Medicare formularies.[22]

To their credit, pharmaceutical companies have considered ways to reduce the cost burden on consumers by providing rebates to pharmaceutical benefit managers (PBMs). PBMs are third-party administrators of prescription drug programs. You are probably familiar with the three largest PBM organizations: Express Scripts, CVS Health, and OptumRx. These companies have major influence on what's included on your list of approved medications, also known as a formulary. As you are probably aware, medications that aren't on your formulary are much more costly. PBMs have the ability to negotiate with pharmaceutical companies and obtain lower prices for prescription drugs through price discounts, rebates from pharmaceutical companies, and mail-service pharmacies. This sounds well and good, but I question their altruism.

Many believe that PBMs place drugs on formularies based on the rebate that they are able to obtain, and not necessarily based on the lowest drug cost. There is also limited data on what percentage of rebates PBMs are kicking back to the consumer and how much they are keeping in their own pocket. This is a legitimate question considering CVS Health's Fortune 500 rank in 2018 was number seven, and Express Scripts' rank was number twenty-five. This question could be easily answered if rebate data was published, but it isn't.

Tim Wentworth is the CEO of Express Scripts and he was interviewed on *CBS This Morning* in 2017. He was asked directly if Express Scripts can make public how pharmaceutical rebates are distributed. His response in part was, "That's really a client decision based on how they are overall funding their program." The answer wasn't yes and the buck was passed.

It shouldn't be surprising that Big Pharma prioritizes a return on their investment. As stated before, according to a *Washington Post* article in 2013, nine out of ten big pharmaceutical companies spent more on marketing than on research and development. They want to move their product in which they are heavily invested. It also shouldn't be surprising that Big Pharma will use whatever loopholes are available to make this profit. This is capitalism, and again, it is not illegal. It is, however, shaping the economics of our health-care system. If this bothers you, please don't sit idle. Campaign contributions from the pharmaceutical industry totaled $62.7 million during the 2016 election cycle.[23] Prioritize voting for leaders that aren't being paid big bucks by Big Pharma. Let your elected officials know how you feel. I'm sure Thom Tillis, the North Carolina senator, is tired of getting my voice mail messages, but I don't care. This has to change!

Defensive Medicine

In the wee hours of a cold and snowy morning during my intern year, an obese African American woman arrived at the emergency department. Her legs and torso were covered by multiple mismatched blankets. She had a scarf around her head, the type my grandmother used to wear before she went to bed at night. Her shoes were worn and void of laces. The rubber soles were coming loose. She was young, perhaps in her late thirties. I pulled up her electronic chart to review her vital signs and chief complaint. She had no known address, so I assumed that she was homeless. What an awful combination—the cold winter wind and no place to call home. My heart broke for her.

I made my way to the patient room. "Ma'am, I'm Dr. Williams. What can I help you with today?"

"My chest hurts," she said as she pointed to her sternum.

"When did you develop chest pain?" I asked.

"Before I went to sleep," she said. "I tried to sleep it off, but that didn't help. I tried some whiskey, but that didn't help either."

"Alcohol won't help your chest pain, ma'am," I said with a smile. She smiled back at me. Her gums were black and she had only a few teeth scattered about.

"How do you know?" she said stoically. "It helps me with everything else." My heart broke even more.

I went to the refrigerator to grab her a turkey sandwich and crackers. The turkey sandwiches were soggy and nothing to write home about, but it was all we had in the ER at 3:00 a.m. I asked the nurse to perform an EKG and I ordered some labs. I was convinced her chest pain was benign, likely just reflux.

"Sure you want that EKG, doc?" the nurse asked with a thick south Philly accent. "She had an EKG three days ago too."

I reviewed her electronic medical record. The nurse was correct. She did have an EKG three days ago. In fact, she had more than twenty EKGs in the emergency department over the past year. Maybe she just wanted to get out of the cold, I thought to myself.

"Hold that EKG," I told the nurse. "I need to discuss this with the attending." It didn't make much sense to me. Not only did she have multiple EKGs, but she had several CT scans of her chest to rule out pulmonary embolism over the past several months. Patients with pulmonary embolism can present to the hospital with chest pain, but my goodness, when is enough enough? I was more worried about her developing cancer from CT scan radiation than her having a heart or lung problem. I found the attending sitting behind his desk reviewing patient records. I stood there for a good two minutes, waiting for him to acknowledge my presence. He had one leg folded over the other while he twirled a pen flawlessly between his fingers. He finally glanced my direction.

"Are you a helicopter?" he asked me.

"Excuse me, sir?" I said.

"Are you a helicopter?" he repeated.

"No, sir. I'm not a helicopter," I said.

"Well, then why are you hovering around me?" he asked. This guy was really sarcastic. Residents loathed the nights he was covering the emergency department.

"I have a concern, sir. The patient in bed seven says she has chest pain. She was here three days ago with similar symptoms. She had an EKG and a CT scan of her chest, which was normal. I don't think she needs another workup. She's been to the emergency department over ten times in the past—"

"Are her legs swollen?" he interrupted. He still hadn't fully turned to acknowledge me.

"Yes. There is mild swelling, but this is also documented in her previous notes. She's here because she's homeless. Let's give her a meal and keep her out of the cold until the morning and see if social work can help her find a shelter."

"Get an EKG, draw labs including a troponin, and get a CT scan of the chest," the ER attending said matter-of-factly. "You've never been sued before, Dr. Williams, have you?" He was correct. I hadn't.

Defensive medicine refers to a medical practitioner who acts in a manner to best mitigate potential legal risk, instead of considering the best option for the patient. The best option for the homeless lady was a meal and support from our social work staff. It was also the most cost-effective option. We chose to add on a CT scan, EKG, and lab work, none of which were necessary. The CT scan was negative for pulmonary embolism.

The EKG was normal. The lab work was normal. The only thing that was concerning about her visit was the attending physician's defensive stance and the cost of her medical care. In this case, there was obvious concern for a potential malpractice suit, though the chances of the patient having any medical ailment were very slim.

There are cases in which medical malpractice is obvious. I've read of surgeons who have resected the wrong rib. I've been told of surgeons who have mistakenly removed a healthy kidney instead of the diseased kidney. Now instead of living a normal life with one functioning kidney, the patient had to undergo a kidney transplant. I once cared for a patient at a veterans hospital who had a cervical neck abscess that was impinging on his spinal cord. I tried to have the patient transferred to a local hospital that was equipped to manage spine disease, but I was told by their neurosurgeon that the patient wasn't truly having cord impingement. It was only after he lost feeling and movement in his legs that I was able to get him transferred. This led to permanent neurologic dysfunction. More recently, I spoke with a patient whose husband was diagnosed with an irregular heart rhythm. He was started on a drug called amiodarone to fix the problem. Amiodarone has been shown to cause hepatitis in some patients, and therefore it is imperative to routinely check liver enzyme levels. His liver enzyme levels were never checked until he walked into an emergency department with confusion, a swollen belly, and a yellow tint to his eyes. He died of amiodarone-induced liver disease three months later. The majority of physicians would agree that tort in the cases described above is unambiguous and that the practitioners should be held accountable.

With that being said, these cases are atypical and the courts can be inundated with frivolous lawsuits that are a waste of physician time and money as well as taxpayer dollars. A study in the *New England Journal of Medicine* found that 37 percent of malpractice claims didn't even involve an error, and that 84 percent of claims that were not associated with error or injury resulted in no compensation.[24] Even if the justice system works and no fault is attributed to the practitioner, the suit itself can raise physician malpractice premiums. To avoid this hike in liability insurance and the cost and time associated with medical malpractice cases, physicians will continue to practice defensive medicine, also known as CYA (cover your ass) medicine.

So how big of a problem is defensive medicine? In a study by Anupam Jena, physicians who were covered by a large liability insurer had their malpractice claims reviewed over a fourteen-year period. Of all physicians, 7.4 percent had a malpractice claim with only 1.6 percent leading to payment. The mean indemnity payment was $274,887.[25] With no tort reform on the horizon, that price tag is enough to persuade a practitioner to cover their ass!

In another study titled "National Costs of the Medical Liability System," the authors estimated the overall medical liability system costs, which include defensive medicine, to be $55 billion in 2008.[26] That's correct: $55 billion or 2.4 percent of total health-care spending!

Do No Harm

One afternoon, I received a phone call from a fellow physician. He is a very smart guy that has trained at top-notch academic programs. He has the reputation of being a doctor that you send patients to if you're struggling with a diagnosis. He's the personification of Dr. Gregory House, the main character in the television series *House*. He always seems to have the correct answer. I've sent quite a few patients his way. He has a steel-trap memory and can recite the diagnostic criteria for the most rare and obscure disease states. I remember once he diagnosed a patient with a rare immunodeficiency called Good's syndrome. The labs and imaging results had yet to return on the patient, but he was positive. "It's Good's," he said confidently, leaving no room for doubt. He was correct.

"Hey, Aerik," he said. "This is Dr. Calloway." I always find it entertaining when physicians refer to themselves as "doctor" when speaking to other doctors, as if I didn't know he is a physician. "I just saw Miranda Cheeks in clinic. I think you saw her sister last week."

"I did," I replied. "She's an elementary-school-aged girl who came in with her mother for an allergy evaluation. If I remember correctly, she tested negative for allergies."

"Yup, that's her," he said. "I just saw her sister in the clinic. I'm going to put her on allergy injections."

"Oh. Okay. Is that all?" I asked.

"That's it. Just thought I would let you know that her mom is going to ask why you didn't recommend allergy injections for her sister Miranda."

I was a bit confused. "Well, I tested Miranda. She has no allergies," I stated matter-of-factly. "Why would I put her on allergy injections if she has no allergies?"

"Her sister's testing was negative too," he replied.

"I don't understand," I said dubiously. "If her testing demonstrates no evidence of allergies, then why are you putting her on allergy injections?"

"Well, you've got to do something," he said.

I sat dumbfounded after I hung up the phone. I was less than one year out of training and he was a senior doctor, but I was positive that allergy injections would not be beneficial in a patient without a history of allergies. I reviewed the literature and found no potential benefit for allergy injections in a patient with no proven environmental allergies. I was so utterly confused that I emailed colleagues in my allergy group. One response stands out:

"So what we have here is both a tort and a criminal act. Negligence and battery. Not something one would want to document or even mention. Probably not as rare as we might hope."

Over time I have found this statement to be accurate. The Dr. Calloways of the world are not as rare as we might hope. The appropriate treatment strategy for patients with nasal symptoms and no evidence of allergy is an intranasal steroid, but prescribing Flonase provides no reimbursement to the treating allergist. Instead, Dr. Calloway chose to put her on allergy shots, which subjects this young girl to weekly trips to the allergy clinic over the next three to five years for injections that amount to placebo. The cost of allergy injections is also thousands of dollars which in this case will be funded by Medicaid of North Carolina. I'm in agreement with the email response of my colleague. This action is not only immoral, but fraudulent, and adds costs to our health-care system.

One of my favorite patients of all time is a woman named Latasha. She sees me in the clinic on rare occasion, typically when her asthma is so bad that she can barely walk from my parking lot to the examination room. She wishes she could be seen in the clinic more often; however, she is poor and without insurance. I've told her at each visit that she is always welcome in my clinic and I will treat her with sample medications left by pharmaceutical representatives. She always tells me that she appreciates being seen, but just hates getting something for free.

Latasha is the type who can tell an ordinary story in a way that will leave you laughing without being able to catch your breath. She is in her mid-forties, tall with light brown skin and a muscular physique. She talks with a smooth drawl similar to Bernie Mac. Her voice is deep and her words are deliberate. Her jokes build slowly until they come to a hysterical conclusion. The finality brings a wide-eyed facial expression to punctuate the punch line. She is vulgar and endearing all at the same time.

She was in her typical mood one afternoon when she came into the office to see me. To my surprise, her asthma had been well controlled. "I ain't here for my asthma, doc," she told me. "My asthma has been good."

"Well, that's a relief," I said. "Why has it taken so long for you to come back and see me?"

"Don't mess with me, doc. You know I'm a fat girl with asthma … I don't play!" This was her favorite joke. "I came to tell you about my neck."

"Well, you know I'm an allergist?" I said sarcastically.

"Well, that means you went to medical school," she said with a smile. "Listen here, doc, my neck has been bothering me. It's bad, doc. Every time I turn my head I feel pain shooting up and down my body." My demeanor changed and I listened intently. "I can barely sleep and my grandbaby asked me why I don't turn my head when she talks to me. She started smacking me on my side and then running away 'cause she knows I can't turn my neck to find her."

"This could be serious," I said. "But in all honesty, I'm an allergist and haven't evaluated a patient for neck pain in many years."

She cut me off. "Doc, I'm not asking you to see me for my neck. I already went and saw the neurosurgeon."

"Oh. Okay. Well, what did they tell you?"

"I'm fittin' to tell you if you stop interrupting." She shot me another smile. "I told the doctor that I was having symptoms that made me walk like Frankenstein, looking only forward and not to the side. I told him that I wanted to do some rehab to get my neck back to feeling normal. Do you know what that man told me, doc?" I raised my eyebrows inquisitively, careful not to interrupt. "He told me that once I get insurance, he's gonna operate on my neck."

"Hmm," I muttered. I paused for a few seconds. "He wants to operate? Bring me the imaging reports and I'll see if I can get a second opinion."

"That's the thing. He don't have no imaging reports!" she exclaimed. "I wasn't in there for more than two minutes and he wants to operate! He barely even examined my neck. Plus, you know I can't have surgery with my asthma this bad. He didn't even ask about my asthma. Look, doc, I've got kin that have gone to this man for neck pain and he operates on everybody. My family comes out worse after surgery. Instead of only being able to look forward, they come out only being able to look to either the right or left. You should see our family Christmas photo. Half of 'em leaning to the right and the other half is leaning to the left." I couldn't help but laugh.

"Oh, you laughin', doc," Latasha said with laughter of her own. "I ought to bring you one of our Christmas pictures. That will really make you laugh!" Latasha continued to laugh until her laughter turned to tears. Her mood changed in an instant. "You know what really made me upset though, doc?"

She was no longer joking and I sensed the shift in mood. "You know what really pissed me off?" She had a few sobs before composing herself. "That man had the nerve to entice me to go through with the surgery so that I could get disability. He told me, 'Don't worry about anything. I can get you disability.' Did he think I was stupid? Is that all I'm worth to him? He was gonna put me through surgery even though I may not need it. He gets paid and I get a disability check. I didn't ask for all that. All I wanted was rehab."

One of the promises of the Hippocratic oath recited by all physicians on their day of graduation from medical school is to "first, do no harm." This implies that the physician should act as a patient advocate. The problem with "first, do no harm" is that it competes with capitalism. If the hospital doesn't perform a CT scan, then there is reduced revenue. When Dr. Calloway stated, "You've got to do something," in regards to ordering allergy injections for a little girl, he may as well have stated, "If I do nothing, then I don't get paid." The neurosurgeon has incentive to do surgery because it pays much more than just an office visit or a referral for rehabilitation. Not only have Dr. Calloway and the neurosurgeon put their patients at risk; they might also be liable for fraud and tort, as detailed in the email quoted above.

We become familiar with the notorious cases. Dr. Farid Fata was a practicing oncologist in Detroit, Michigan, who diagnosed healthy people with different types of cancer. He amassed $17 million by fraudulently billing them for chemotherapy. Imagine the emotions of being diagnosed with cancer and experiencing the side effects of chemotherapy, only to learn that you never had cancer in the first place! He pleaded guilty to health-care fraud and money laundering in September 2014 and was sentenced to forty-five years in prison.[27]

In 2016, a Miami psychiatrist pleaded guilty to federal charges of healthcare and immigration fraud and to filing false claims. His crime in part involved prescribing antipsychotic medicine for patients without any underlying disease. He advised the patients not to take the medicine. The "diagnosis" allowed for his clients to obtain Social Security disability and hence Medicaid and Medicare. He cost taxpayers over $50 million.[28]

These cases are obvious, but the not-so-obvious cases are likely more common than expected. Who is there to police the practitioner that adds on charges for procedures that were not necessary or never performed? Practitioners are left to police themselves. This is certainly a problem, evidenced by the $3.7 billion the Justice Department received from false claims act cases in 2017.[29] The more insurance reimburses for fraudulent care, the more your insurance premium, your specialist co-payment, your deductible, and your out-of-pocket maximum payments will increase.

The Least of These

The Patient Protection and Affordable Care Act (ACA) went into effect in March 2010. The intent of this act was to lower health-care costs, a goal of which all Americans are in favor. Its polarizing methodology, however, separated Americans down political lines. Its nickname, "Obamacare," was used to engender support from the left and disdain from the right. One of my favorite YouTube videos of all time is performed by Jimmy Kimmel TV. The interviewer describes the policies of "Obamacare" to individuals walking down the street at random. The interviewer is careful to not use the word "Obamacare," but only describe its policies. Many fervently support these policies, but when asked if they support "Obamacare," they are disgusted at the question. In fact, some state they support the Affordable Care Act, but they don't support Obamacare!

In short, the ACA was designed to make health care more affordable in a few different ways. First, the federal government would provide money to states to expand Medicaid. By the end of 2019, thirty-seven states had taken the feds up on their offer; however, the remaining states decided not to participate in Medicaid expansion.[30] Federal money for expansion decreases as the years go forward, making some states hesitant about expansion and ultimately being stuck with a bill they couldn't afford. Some state governments simply played politics and were antagonistic for the sake of being antagonistic. Secondly, the ACA mandates all Americans to purchase health insurance or to pay a penalty. This policy is known as the "individual mandate." If we purchase health insurance in bulk, then risk is spread across a greater number of individuals, theoretically leading to decreased premiums. Lastly, the federal government would pay health insurance companies to subsidize plans purchased through the ACA exchange.

Did the ACA fail? It depends on who you talk to. According to the National Center for Health Statistics, the number of people without health insurance fell from 48 million in 2010 to 28.6 million in 2016, and insurance plans were purchased by 11.6 million people through the Health Insurance Marketplace or a state-based exchange.[31] More people with insurance is a good thing. Conversely, if you talk to my buddy Richard, a Vietnam veteran and a hardcore conservative (his Facebook page is littered with anti-Democratic rhetoric), he will tell you that Obamacare is a disaster. The average Obamacare premium cost has increased 33 percent since 2010, and some states will see premiums increase by 90 percent over the next three years.[32] "Why are they increasing my rates? People are relying too much on the government," Richard said while hitting golf balls on the driving range one morning.

I don't pretend to know the answers as to why or if a policy fails. I'm certainly not a policy expert, and it seems to me that the experts can't come to a consensus. I do, however, have great understanding of what happens when policy leaves individuals without insurance. I treated a young woman with severe persistent asthma who had difficulty with her activities of daily living. She was dependent on systemic steroids to help control her asthma and had gained so much weight from the steroids that it was difficult to discern her neck from her shoulders. Walking through the aisles of the grocery store was a challenge. She would have to stop after walking down each aisle to catch her breath, and she spent many nights without sleep because of the severity of her asthma symptoms. I started her on the aforementioned Cinqair and she got her life back. She would skip into my office with pictures of wedding apparel she had picked out for the big day. She could breathe and she was so thankful. Life was good … until she lost her job at Food Lion. No job equals no insurance. No insurance equals no Cinqair. No Cinqair equals going back on systemic steroids and albuterol nebulizer treatments at three o'clock in the morning.

I treated a sixty-four-year-old man for an immunodeficiency. Before he was seen in my office, he had recurring bouts of meningitis and pneumonia. He was in and out of the hospital, suffering from infections. Fortunately, his boss was understanding and gave him leeway. He was able to keep his job and hence his insurance benefits. He was referred to my clinic soon after I arrived in Salisbury, as I was the only practicing immunologist. After review of his history and laboratory data, I diagnosed him with common variable immunodeficiency, a condition where the body makes too little immunoglobulin, rendering the immune system unable to fight infections. I started him on treatment, infusing immunoglobulin into the subcutaneous tissue in his abdomen on a weekly basis. It worked. He had his life back. No more meningitis or pneumonia … until he lost his job. No job equals no insurance. No insurance equals no immunoglobulin infusions. No immunoglobulin infusions equal hospitalizations for recurrent infections.

"Medicare for all" has been a rallying cry for several democrats running for office in 2020. I'm not against that sort of policy. I believe everyone should have access to decent medical care, the same way we all have access to paved roads and protective services. Nobody should have to stay in their bed wheezing or fear recurrent infections if a medical treatment does exist. With our current system, however, the cost of "Medicare for all" is too high. A Bloomberg study estimates the tab would run us about $32 trillion.[33]

I would suggest that "Medicare for all" will only work if we reduce the cost of health care. We can reduce costs with national drug pricing so that patients have access to pricing information. We can reduce the costs if loopholes that allow pharmaceutical companies to profit at the cost of the consumer are closed. We can reduce cost with policy that mandates PBMs to return all rebates to the consumer. We can reduce costs if practitioners hold each other accountable for unscrupulous billing practices. We can reduce the costs with tort reform. If we are able to reduce health-care costs, and "Medicare for all" costs only a fraction of the estimated Bloomberg study, perhaps it would be achievable and palatable for both the left and the right.

I've given a description of how physicians, pharmaceutical companies, and insurers contribute to our health-care bill. Understand, this represents a fraction of the cost. I don't cover all aspects of factors contributing to health-care costs because this is *Aerik's Anatomy*, describing my personal experience with the health-care system. I therefore encourage all interested to read Elisabeth Rosenthal's book entitled *An American Sickness: How Healthcare Became Big Business and How You Can Take It Back*. She delves deeply into the costs of health care with disparaging firsthand accounts. After reading her book and being armed with knowledge, I encourage all to talk to your senators and let your voices be heard. Hold them responsible. Hold your doctor responsible. Hold your insurer responsible. Hold your hospital responsible.

I mentioned my buddy Richard. I consider him to be a friend who has served this country to the fullest extent. He has earned his stripes. While we were hitting golf balls that morning and arguing over health care in this country, he recited my favorite Scripture. "Truly I tell you, whatever you did for one of the least of these brothers and sisters of mine, you did for me" (Matthew 25:40). He argues that traditionally "doing for the least of these" has been performed by the church and social services. To that I say, let's end this tradition. Let's all be advocates for those who are without health care. Let's inspire our leaders to prioritize reducing health-care costs and ensuring all Americans have equal access to health care. We are responsible for each other. It is righteous.

CHAPTER 4

The Poor

"Po"

On occasion, my mom likes to remind me that at one point in their lives, she and my dad were "po." When she says "po," she puts strong emphasis on the "p." She describes po people as worse off than poor people. They lived in an apartment in 1978 when my sister was born. My mother was a schoolteacher and my father was in his last year of medical school. That's two adults and one infant living on government loans and a teacher's salary. They were po. By the time I was born, my father had started his job as a resident and also performed moonlighting services at local hospitals to bring in additional income. That elevated their financial status from po to poor.

My mother speaks in relative terms. We did have food on the table and a roof over our heads. They bought a modest house in Gahanna, Ohio, not far from where that man called us niggers at the post office. We didn't lack for anything. In retrospect, I wouldn't describe us as poor, though we were not well off. I remember once we had worms living under the carpet and my dad had to pull the carpet up and scoop the worms out himself. My mother will tell you that this is po people behavior.

Being poor, if we were ever truly poor, was only temporary. My father graduated from residency and started his medical practice in Columbus, Ohio. The poor generational state of the Williams family dates back centuries and was changed by my mother and father's pursuit of education, and it will affect generations to come.

For most of the poor, this seismic shift in wealth will not be realized. Their pattern of poverty is cyclical. There is either no opportunity or there is no willingness to create one. Children born into poor households observe habits of their poor parents and they themselves will emulate these habits as they grow older. Their children will observe their poor habits, and they too will find themselves in poverty.

I have a forty-five-minute commute from my home in Davidson to my office in Salisbury. I've found it refreshing and enlightening to listen to audiobooks during my drive. It frees my mind from the upcoming schedule and allows me to exercise a different part of my brain. I was recently recommended to read *Evicted: Poverty and Profit in the American City* by Matthew Desmond. It is an absolutely captivating book. I had only listened to the first couple of chapters when I arrived at the office, but I couldn't stop listening. I sat in the parking lot, enthralled by every detail. Desmond is a sociology professor at Princeton who studies poverty. He spent countless hours living with the poor to have a better understanding of their daily challenges. His firsthand accounts are very raw, sparing no details. He speaks of malnourished children with hunger pains, pregnant mothers with no place to live, and landlords who exploit and unfairly profit off the poor.

I was sitting in the car listening when I was startled by my nurse. She knocked on the car window to alert me that I had patients waiting. I exited the car and connected the audiobook to my Bluetooth headphones and walked around the clinic listening to the tales of those living in poverty. When it was time to see a patient, I slipped the headphones into my pocket, and after the patient appointment, I was back to listening to the audiobook. I was hooked.

Matthew Desmond details the life of a character named Scott, a thirty-nine-year-old who lives in a mobile home park. Scott was a registered nurse who at one time had his life together. He was paid well and was living what most would consider to be the American dream. Scott, however, had a problem. He was a drug addict. He was stealing opioid pain medications from the hospitals in which he worked. These pain medications were intended for patients who actually had pain, but Scott wanted them for his high. In a predictable fashion, Scott's life hit rock bottom in a steep downward spiral. He found himself homeless at times and on the streets doing drugs with shady characters. Scott's story doesn't end here. He tired of the instability that opioid pain medications had created. He makes the difficult decision to spend his money on treatment at a methadone clinic. He was unable to afford both mobile home rent and methadone treatment, so a shelter became his home. Scott becomes clean and his life is renewed.

Sarah

As I read about Scott, I couldn't help but think about one of my patients named Sarah. Their lives do bear resemblance. Sarah is a twentysomething who saw me in the clinic for severe asthma. After reviewing her lung function test with my medical student, I was surprised she was able to walk into my office. Her lungs were inflamed and significantly obstructed. Sarah had been in and out of the hospital with asthma exacerbations for many years. She had a life plagued by constant shortness of breath and wheezing. It's difficult to convey how miserable life can be when living with uncontrolled asthma. The best that I can describe is to imagine that you are drowning and gasping to take a breath. This feeling may last for several hours. It occurs multiple times per day, and when it will happen is unpredictable, sometimes awakening you in the middle of the night. You sleep next to your nebulizer because it's the only thing that allows for temporary relief.

Sarah's asthma was so severe that she was unable to exercise. Her limited activity led to obesity. She had a big hump on the back of her neck, a consequence of daily prednisone. Her face was rounded with fat deposits. Her oral exam revealed a tongue ring, and when I asked her to say "ahh," the stench of cigarette smoke was overwhelming.

I explained to Sarah that she had severe asthma; however, there was a medicine that she had yet to try that I believed would improve her symptoms. It would require her to receive an injection in my office once per month. Sarah was excited and I was excited for her. I counseled her on smoking cessation, but it was worthless. "I've got a lot of stress," she told me. She inquired about the cost of her visit and the cost of the medication. She told me that she didn't have much. I assured her that the cost of her visit would be covered by Medicare.

Sarah was scheduled to see me again two weeks after her original visit, but she failed to show up. Typically, I'm not surprised when patients don't show to their appointments. As I mentioned, many of my patients are poor. When my staff calls to remind patients of their upcoming appointments, it's not uncommon for their phone to be disconnected or for a patient to cancel because they don't have transportation. I was surprised by Sarah, however. I had explained to her the severity of her asthma, and she was excited about the opportunity of trying a new medication. I was truly dumbfounded when she missed her appointment.

I considered not including the following in this book because I'm ashamed. This shame was revealed to me as I was processing Matthew Desmond's book. I judged Sarah. I thought she was typical. Her asthma was poorly controlled because she had no initiative. Even when a physician with experience in managing asthma gives her hope, she can't manage to get her shit together. She was lazy. That's why she wouldn't quit smoking cigarettes. I don't care how much stress you have, if you can't breathe, then maybe you should quit smoking. Her laziness is why she was obese. Her laziness is why she was poor. These were the first thoughts that came to my mind. I could only shake my head in disbelief, but in retrospect, I shook my head in arrogance. The truth of the matter, as I would later find out, is that I had no idea why she couldn't make it to her doctor's appointment. I had no idea of the stressors in her life. I had no idea why she couldn't keep a job. I had no idea why she was poor.

Sarah called my clinic about two weeks later and left a message with my nurse. I wasn't surprised that she had called. She had significant impairment from her asthma, and it was only a matter of time before she reached out to me. One of the things that you can't live without is breathing. I called her back towards the end of the workday.

"Hey, Dr. Williams," she said sheepishly.

"Hello, Sarah. I was worried about you. How have you been?" I wanted to ask, "Where have you been?"

"I'm calling you because I'm very sorry I missed my appointment." There was a pause. "I'm currently in rehab."

There was another pause, this time followed by a sob. "I haven't been completely honest with you. I'm hooked on pain pills."

I … felt … terrible! Here I was judging this young woman for missing her appointment, questioning whether she was committed to her health or committed to being lazy. Like Scott, she was poor. Like Scott, she was hooked on drugs. Like Scott, she was judged by the people around her. Like Scott, she had the initiative to seek rehabilitation to turn her life around. God had put this woman in my life not only to treat her asthma but also for me to learn something about myself. What was bothersome was that I couldn't stop judging. I just kept going. I thought she was poor because she spent her money on cigarettes and narcotics. If she would stop spending her money on cigarettes and narcotics, then maybe she would be able to pay for her health care. "Stop it!" I said to myself.

"I need to see you as soon as possible, Sarah. I want to help you. Can you come in tomorrow? I have an opening in my schedule."

"Yes," she said. "I'm leaving rehab today. I'll be in tomorrow morning."

"Perfect." I said. "I'm looking forward to seeing you."

When Sarah arrived at the clinic, she looked disheveled, as if she had just woken up. She still had the sleep in her eyes. She was wearing blue pajamas with cartoon characters. She yawned as the nurse led her to the patient room. I could smell the cigarette smoke emanating from her pajamas. She smiled and waved at me.

"Hey, Sarah," I said as I entered the examination room. "It's good to see you."

"Nice to see you," she said.

"How do you feel after rehab?"

"I feel like I'm going to get through this. I feel like this is a new me." She smiled with renewed energy. She ran her hand through her hair, which had been colored blue and trimmed significantly since the last time I saw her. "I'm sorry I didn't tell you about the drug use. I was embarrassed." She was staring at the floor, unable to look me in the eye.

"That's okay," I said reassuringly. "I believe in you. I believe you can get through this."

"That's the first time I've heard that," she said. "The pulmonologist told me that I was going to be dead in two years. He said my asthma was beyond repair, and since I wasn't going to quit smoking, I would be dead in just two years. You really think I can get through this?"

Honestly, the pulmonologist had an accurate assessment. The combination of severe persistent asthma and cigarette smoking is a recipe for early death. "I do think we can get you better, but Sarah, we have to get you to stop smoking. The smoking is going to kill you." My tone was paternal. I could feel myself getting frustrated.

"I can't stop, Dr. Williams! I've got stress." She seemed defeated and was starting to sense my frustration.

"You don't need to stress over your asthma. I think we can get you under control with injections of a new medicine."

"Asthma isn't my main stressor." Her voice was cracking, and her eyes began to tear up. I knew there was more to the story, and I waited for her to begin. She gathered her composure and started. "When I was four years old, my parents would drop me off at our neighbor's house. My parents thought he was a nice guy. They were good friends. They used to watch television together and talk until the early morning hours. I remember him being really funny. He used to make me laugh and make my parents laugh, so my mom and dad thought that he was safe. Well, it turns out he wasn't." Sarah became despondent and her face turned downcast. She had a few tears that rolled down her cheeks. I passed her a tissue. "Thank you," she said between sobs. She was still staring at the floor, unable to look me in the eye. It took her a few seconds before she continued.

"The first time it happened, I had no idea what was going on. He told me he had candy in his basement. What kind of kid doesn't like candy, you know? So I followed him downstairs. He asked me to sit on his couch and he turned on the television. I remember the cartoons that were playing. 'Where's the candy?' I remember asking him. He opened an orange bottle and gave me what he said was candy through a syringe. It wasn't candy. I remember him setting up a video camera next to the couch and then I remember becoming sleepy. I didn't pass out. I remember everything, but I was so calm. He took his clothes off, all of his clothes off. Then he took my clothes off. After adjusting the video camera, he sat next to me on the couch and told me to do horrible things that I don't like to talk about. When it was over and his 'candy' wore off, he told me that if I ever told anyone, he would kill me. The pattern continued for over a year, until my parents stumbled on some of the pictures he took while in his basement. It wasn't just me. There were pictures of several kids." She stopped talking to wipe her eyes.

"Have you seen a therapist about this?" I asked.

"I have. It's nothing that I can let go of. People talk about prayer, and believe me, Dr. Williams, I've prayed. I want to put this behind me and look forward to the rest of my life, but I can't."

I understood. I believe in God, but I also have full understanding that we are flesh. The sadness I saw in Sarah's countenance was unfathomable. "Okay, Sarah. I understand, but I still think we can make this thing happen."

"I think so too, but I'm going to continue smoking for now. It calms my nerves and I don't want to take any medication that I can become addicted to. I'm not going on Xanax."

"Okay, Sarah. Perhaps we can talk about cutting back on the cigarettes."

"Not now. I can't do it now. He's been in prison for nearly twenty years and he gets out next month. Now is not a good time."

So Sarah wasn't lazy; she was depressed and anxious. Her depression and anxiety stemmed from an unimaginable childhood experience, and she coped by smoking cigarettes and using prescription opioid drugs. Her drug use and depression made it impossible for her to keep employment. Her unemployment led to poverty. Her poverty led to her concern about her medical bill. My impression was that she was lazy and without initiative and I was wrong. I was also very embarrassed. What humbled me the most was when she thanked me for believing in her. She brought me a card a few days before Thanksgiving and gave me a big hug. I'm thankful that she didn't know that I shamed her in my mind; otherwise I probably would have lost her.

Were there other patients of mine whose health care was affected by poverty?

Job's

In late 2017, I received a call from the health department. I'm the only immunologist in Salisbury, so I frequently receive calls from physicians asking for my opinion on clinical cases. Typically, the calls are asking for advice on issues that I find to be routine. Through my training, I've encountered several immunologic and allergic cases, even the rarest.

"Hey, Dr. Williams," said a lady on the other end of the telephone.

"Yes, ma'am. What can I do for you?" I was listening to the physician and catching up on the sports news at the same time.

"I have a kid here that I would like your opinion on."

"Okay. Go ahead and tell me about the kiddo," I said while reading ESPN.com.

"He's a four-year-old boy with Job's syndrome."

I stopped her immediately and gave her my full attention. "Excuse me. Did you say Job's syndrome?"

"Yes. Do you see Job's syndrome?"

Job's syndrome is also referred to as Hyper IgE syndrome. We call it Job's syndrome because individuals afflicted with this disease have physical characteristics that resemble the biblical character Job. Oftentimes they have a persistent rash that resembles eczema, or their skin can have boils. They typically have a broad nose, prominent forehead, and deep-set eyes. The cause of Job's syndrome is a defect in a protein that helps to regulate T cell function. T cells are important immune cells that help to fight infection. Given poor T cell function, patients with Job's syndrome are at risk for infections such as pneumonias and abscesses. A subset of patients with Job's syndrome will not produce enough antibodies to fight infections and will require routine antibody infusions. Job's syndrome is very rare. Approximately two hundred cases have been described in the literature.

I had only seen one child with Job's syndrome, and technically I didn't really "see" him. In 2011, I was interviewing for an allergy and immunology training position at the National Institutes of Health (NIH) in Washington, DC. As part of the interview process, I attended patient rounds. I remember my ears perking up when the NIH fellow discussed the case of a lung infection in a patient with Job's syndrome. I stood outside the patient's room but did not enter. I remember thinking to myself that I'd probably never see a case of Job's syndrome in my career.

"Yes, I treat Job's syndrome. Well, I've never actually seen a case of Job's syndrome, but I know what needs to be done. Send him to my clinic immediately." Thinking back, the physician on the other end of the line probably had no confidence after that response.

"Okay. Just a couple of other things. His mom says he has the type where he requires immunoglobulin infusions every month. Can you get him these infusions?"

"That shouldn't be a problem. What kind of insurance does he have?"

"Well … that's the problem. He doesn't have insurance."

"Okay … Well, that shouldn't be too much of an issue. As long as he has a Social Security number, I should be able to secure him medicine for infusions at no cost to his parents. Tell them not to worry about payment to my clinic. I'll take care of that."

"Well … there's still a problem. He doesn't have a Social Security number."

"Oh. Well, then this could be a problem." I sighed. Not only had I not seen a case of Job's syndrome, I had also not seen a patient without a Social Security number. "So tell me, how was he being managed before? How was he receiving infusions? How was he even diagnosed with Job's syndrome if he doesn't have insurance or a Social Security number for that matter? The molecular testing for diagnosis is expensive, and without insurance, he would have to pay out of pocket."

"Are you ready for the next twist, Dr. Williams?" the physician asked. She had me intrigued. "So the patient is from Mexico City and had lived there until his arrival in Salisbury yesterday. He was diagnosed with Job's syndrome at birth. I don't believe he had the molecular testing required for diagnosis. His IgE blood level was high, he had physical characteristics that were consistent with Job's syndrome, and he was having recurrent lung infections and cold abscesses. Therefore, the assumption was made that he had Job's syndrome. He was told that he would require monthly infusions. Once he started infusions, the infections stopped. He's since been a fairly healthy kid."

"I see," I said, trying to grasp the gravity of the case. This was certainly atypical. "So this is unrelated, but I'm curious. How does a kid from Mexico City end up here in Salisbury?"

"Dr. Williams, have you been watching the news?"

Was I watching the news? I racked my brain until it hit me. "Holy cow. The earthquake?"

"Yes. The earthquake." The Puebla earthquake in September 2017 had a magnitude of 7.1 MW and claimed 370 lives. Over forty buildings collapsed, including the hospital where the patient was receiving treatment. "Once the hospital collapsed, the mom was told to take her son home to die. She was told there was nothing they could do for him. They would not be able to secure the medicine necessary to keep him from getting recurrent infections and had no means to treat him once an infection occurs. Mom was distraught. She has family in Salisbury, so she packed her belongings. Their first stop was the health department. They are here legally, Dr. Williams. She does have a visa."

I sat in silence for a few seconds. My first case of Job's and my first case of a patient with absolutely no access to medicine, all at the same time. I have sample medicines dropped off by pharmaceutical representatives, but those are for patients with asthma and seasonal allergies. I do not have access to immunoglobulin infusions for people without a Social Security number, and I don't have access to prophylactic antimicrobials necessary for the management of Job's syndrome. "Dr. Williams. Are you still there?"

"Yes. I'm still here. I'm just thinking." In truth, I was thinking about where I could send him. My one provider clinic was not equipped to handle this case. I was sure the academic centers of Duke University or Wake Forest University would be able to provide the necessary resources. "Please send him to my clinic as soon as possible."

That afternoon a boy and his mom came to my clinic. The boy's name was Daniel. He was an undersized four-year-old. He had tan-colored skin with multiple scars, evidence of previous skin abscesses. Other than that, he looked like any other kid that walks into my clinic. In fact, he reminded me of my son. He wore a superhero T-shirt and enjoyed playing with the Lego blocks and Play-Doh in the patient room. He was very loud and very obnoxious. His mother kept telling him to be quiet as he drove the truck made from Lego blocks over the office furniture making the "vroom" sound. He wasn't shy. He used my leg as a ramp and rolled his Lego truck right over it, causing the truck to go soaring into the sky. He threw it up in the air and then secured the truck in his palm...and then he farted. "Daniel!" his mom shouted. He kept playing, undeterred.

I reviewed Daniel's history with his mother. There was no deviation from the report I had received from the Health Department. I gave Daniel's mother my assessment; he needed to be seen at Wake Forest University or Duke University immediately. We also needed to check Daniel's immuno-globulin level. The half-life of immunoglobulin is only two weeks, and he hadn't received his antibody infusion for a month. I knew that I wouldn't be able to secure the antibody infusions for Daniel, but if I was able to show the academic medical centers that his level was threateningly low, then perhaps they would be moved to see him expeditiously. Mom was in agreement. Her primary concern was for her son, but her secondary concern was their poverty.

She spoke to me through an interpreter. "Dr. Williams, checking Daniel's antibody level costs money. We don't have any. We can't even afford to get Daniel back and forth to your clinic. I plan on getting a job, but right now we have nothing."

"I understand. My primary concern too is Daniel's health. Let's get the antibody level first and we will make a plan following." I gave her a slip for the lab. She shook my hand and led her son out of the patient room. He gestured towards the Play-Doh. I told him he could have it.

I eagerly anticipated Daniel's lab result. It typically takes less than twenty-four hours for the result to become available. Twenty-four hours came and went without a notice from the lab. No big deal. Surely the result would be available the next day. Then forty-eight hours had gone by without notification from the laboratory. I was befuddled. I called the lab to see if Daniel and his mother had shown for a blood draw. They hadn't. I asked my nurse to give them a call. I couldn't understand why someone would travel from Mexico to North Carolina with their son who has Job's syndrome with an associated antibody deficiency and not have an essential lab drawn. "Doc," my nurse said. "Daniel hasn't had the lab drawn because his mom can't afford it. Do you remember when she said she had no money?"

My goodness. It wasn't that I had forgotten. I just had no concept of what it truly meant to be poor and without health insurance. Most mothers would have told their son to put the Play-Doh back, but Daniel had nothing to play with at home. Mom didn't hesitate when I allowed him to keep it. She smiled at me and said, "God bless you."

Is this what it's like to live in poverty, without health insurance? Imagine that a person without insurance and no means to pay for health care finds themselves having symptoms of diabetes. Do they go to the doctor's office or are they scared away by the potential hefty bill? Perhaps they would rather just live with the symptoms than face the financial burden. Symptoms are the body's way of alerting our brains that something is wrong. Symptoms will only go away once the problem is fixed. So the diabetic person avoids the doctor and the doctor bill until one day the symptoms are too much to bear. They show up in the emergency department comatose from diabetic ketoacidosis. Or perhaps their unmanaged diabetes leads to a heart attack and they show up to the emergency department with chest pain. What a price to pay!

What if the uninsured person is like Daniel and does decide to be evaluated by a physician? Typically, this person would be asked to pay up front. According to one study, the average price quoted by a doctor's office for uninsured patients is $163 per appointment.[34] Perhaps that's not a steep cost to you or me, but for many this is impossible. The same study demonstrates that only 12 percent of people who ask to make payments on this $163 dispersed over time will be able to secure a doctor's appointment. Let's say this diabetic patient is fortunate enough to find a physician that will care for the uninsured. The physician would like to draw a hemoglobin A1C to get an idea of their blood sugar levels over the past three months and a complete metabolic panel to ensure there are no electrolyte abnormalities and no evidence of kidney dysfunction. These lab tests could cost another $100. Again, perhaps not much to you or me, but this money may be reserved for a family's rent payment or grocery bill. This is not an insignificant sacrifice. Let's say the labs do demonstrate kidney impairment and the person is asked to follow up with a kidney specialist. That's even more money out of their pocket. What if the kidney doctor orders labs or imaging? How much is that going to cost?

The primary care doctor wants to start the patient on insulin to control their blood sugar. How does the person pay for the prescribed insulin or the glucometer? This will cost hundreds of dollars a month without insurance. The primary care doctor would also like to see the patient back in the office in three months to evaluate their blood sugar and repeat a hemoglobin A1C level. How on earth do the poor and uninsured maneuver through our health-care system? Unfortunately, many of them don't.

I called the laboratory and spoke to a manager. I asked whether there were programs available for patients without insurance. She gave me a one-word answer: "No." She didn't say, "I'm sorry, but we don't have any programs at this time." She just said no. She seemed to be unconcerned. I asked her what patients do if they can't pay for labs. She told me, "Then they can't get labs drawn."

"Well, that sucks," I said. Again, she didn't say anything until I broke the silence. "Well, how much does the lab cost? Can my clinic pay for it?"

She said the lab test cost about $30. I gave her our credit card number to pay for the lab. I had my nurse organize an Uber ride to and from the laboratory for Daniel. His mother was more appreciative than any person that I have ever seen in my life. She thanked us and thanked us. She was still thanking us when I hung up the phone. A week later his antibody level came back. It was normal. I reassured Daniel's mother but warned her that it was possible his antibody level could drop in the coming months. Therefore, we should check the level again in three months and in the interim try to get Daniel evaluated at Wake Forest. My nurse called Wake Forest and learned that there was a screening process of sorts for patients without insurance. Daniel's health information was relayed for screening. I was certain that he would be able to receive care.

One week went by and we heard nothing from Wake Forest. Two weeks went by without a response. Then one month, two months, and three months elapsed without a response. I called Daniel's mother and asked her if she had heard anything from Wake Forest. She told me that they had called and said they wouldn't be able to care for Daniel. I was shocked. I couldn't imagine a kid more in need. "We will not give up!" I told her. "Let's try Duke University." In the interim, I rechecked Daniel's antibody level and was relieved to find that it was normal. Over three months his health hadn't changed, but it was still imperative for him to be evaluated. I called Duke and was transferred to the International Patient Services Department.

"Sure!" said a man on the other end of the phone. "Just send in his patient records and have his mom give me a call." I did as I was told.

One week went by and we heard nothing from Duke. Two weeks went by without a response. Then one month, two months, and three months elapsed without a response. I called the representative from International Patient Services and spoke to the same gentleman who all but assured me that Daniel would be seen at Duke. He said there was a clerical error and to have Daniel's mom reach out to him. "Sure!" he said again. I was cautiously optimistic. Daniel's mother never heard back from Duke University. I called again recently and my phone call was never returned.

Is this how we treat the poor? We shut doors in their face. This is consistent with the characters in Matthew Desmond's book. Imagine if Daniel's antibody levels were abnormal and he needed treatment. Where would he go for help? If he did receive help, would it come before he develops pneumonia or meningitis?

The antagonist will tell me that it's not their responsibility to help Daniel. Daniel should help himself. He and his mother should pull Daniel up by his four-year-old boot straps. I won't argue with this perspective because that discussion is often not productive. I would simply state that I don't believe I have a share to give in this world. The blessings in my life have been perpetual. Why then should I not give perpetually, the same way I have received?

Double-Wide

There is a gregarious seven-year-old little boy that I see in my clinic named Dante. He lights up the office as soon as he steps in. He's very handsome. He has light brown skin, curly dark hair, and mannerisms that are far beyond his age. I like Dante because we have adult conversations. It makes me chuckle to speak to this precocious child about his asthma and his peanut allergy. I have adult patients that don't understand their disease as well as Dante.

Dante loves to mimic me as we speak. He crosses one leg over the other, scratches his chin, and looks up in the air while he talks. This just so happens to be my posture when I'm pondering something. He goes into detail about his asthma, using vocabulary far beyond his years. He understands the difference between his maintenance inhaler, which he uses every day to help prevent asthma symptoms, and his albuterol rescue inhaler, which he uses only if he's actually having asthma symptoms. He understands the signs and symptoms of an asthma flare and the protocol to follow if such a flare occurs. He also understands that his asthma is most likely to flare in the fall. This follows the typical asthma pattern for most patients. Dante, however, is at more risk for an asthma flare in the fall because he also has a mold allergy, and mold spores are most prevalent during the late summer and fall seasons.

Dante has a single mother and she works her ass off. She would do anything for her son. Dante had never missed a doctor's appointment. I put him on allergy shots to desensitize him to mold in hopes this would help to control his asthma. The time commitment to allergy shots turns many patients away as it requires a weekly visit to my clinic for thirty weeks, followed by a monthly visit for a total of five years. Dante's mother made sure he was present at each appointment. As a result of their effort and compliance, Dante's asthma symptoms improved, though the fall was always a bit tricky. On occasion, he would require prednisone for an asthma flare.

A prednisone prescription seemed to always bother Dante's mother. She wasn't necessarily concerned about the side effects; I told her that occasional prednisone does no long-term damage to the body. Dante's mother hated prednisone because she saw it more as a personal failure. Every time Dante required prednisone she felt as if she had done something wrong. This guilt stemmed from the visible mold and cockroaches in their apartment. Given Dante's high levels of mold and cockroach allergic antibody, she was sure that his home environment was contributing to his asthma flares. She was correct.

Dante's mother was poor, but she certainly wasn't lazy. As I said, she worked her ass off. She had two jobs and passed Dante off to family when she couldn't care for him. But despite her arduous work ethic, she was unable to find a place to live without cockroaches and visible mold. These allergens contributed to Dante's shortness of breath and wheezing. He spent many nights awake struggling to breathe. His mother would grab his nebulizer and allow albuterol to flow into his lungs. Following the albuterol treatment, he would transiently feel better, but before long he would again inhale enough mold spores to cause a recurrence of respiratory symptoms. The home environment weighed on the conscience of Dante's mother.

At my clinic we have a ham giveaway at Thanksgiving. Patients fill out a card with their name and phone number and place the card in a jar. A week before the holiday, we determine the winners by pulling three cards from the jar at random. I reserve the right to choose at least one winner based on need. Last year I chose Dante. I reviewed his chart a week before Thanksgiving to find his address. That's when it dawned on me that I hadn't seen Dante in my clinic for quite some time. In fact, I hadn't seen him in nine months. It was bizarre, given his mom's persistence and dedication to his asthma management. I called the number listed on the chart. The phone had been disconnected. Just like that, I lost touch with Dante.

The winter holidays and the entire spring had passed without any communication from Dante's mother. I worried about him. It's not uncommon to lose patients to follow-up for a variety of reasons, but not when patients had asthma as severe as Dante's. I went over to the local hospital to review records. I pulled up Dante's chart to see if he had been admitted for an asthma flare. There were no hospital encounters for at least a year. This was a good sign. I called Dante's pediatrician. She too had not heard from Dante in the past year. I didn't know what to make of this. Had they moved?

My clinic is packed in the summer when the grass pollen levels are high. It's so packed that it becomes difficult to plan for the day. At these times I often only glance at my schedule in the morning before I start seeing patients. That's why I had no idea that Dante was in a patient room before I entered. I looked at the name on the chart, but it didn't trigger that this was the Dante that I had been worried about for many months.

"Dante!" I exclaimed. "What's up, buddy? Where have you been?" He smiled a wide grin. His mother smiled too. I gave him a hug. He had grown a few inches and lost some of the baby fat around his cheeks.

"Dr. Williams! What's up?" Dante said.

"Where you been, man? We missed seeing you around the clinic."

Dante's mother interrupted. "I'm sorry, Dr. Williams. I should have called you. I just couldn't afford to come to your clinic anymore."

I was saddened by her explanation. She had aged over the past year. The wrinkles in her brow had become more prominent. The stress was obvious. "You know I would have seen Dante, even if you couldn't pay. He has asthma, and with all of his environmental allergies, his symptoms will continue to flare."

"Well, I thought the root cause of his asthma was his allergies. The mold is what causes him to cough and wheeze?"

"That's correct," I said.

"So I decided to remove him from the mold and cockroach environment. That's what I thought was the best plan for his asthma. I couldn't afford to move anywhere because most of my paycheck went to rent. So I decided to stop paying for as many things as possible and save up to move to a better place. We stopped going to the doctor. This saved the three-dollar co-payment each week. We also saved in gas by not coming to any doctor appointments. I started buying more affordable food. When Dante needed new clothes, we asked the neighbors for clothes they were no longer wearing. We did everything possible to save money. Over the course of the year, I saved about $800. That's all I needed for the down payment on our new place. We still have to cut back some, but our new place has no mold and no cockroaches."

"It's a double-wide!" exclaimed Dante. He stretched his arms as far as he could from his chest.

"How was his asthma during this period?"

"We had to use the nebulizer a lot. I had some old prednisone that I would give him from time to time, but he made it through. And Dr. Williams, do you know what?" asked his mother.

I raised my eyebrows.

"Since we moved, Dante hasn't had any problems with his asthma. No albuterol nebulizer treatments at all."

I put my stethoscope up to Dante's chest. I heard no wheezing. I asked the nurse to perform spirometry in order to evaluate lung function. His spirometry was normal. The lung obstruction that was present just a few years prior was barely noticeable. I only see Dante in follow-up once per year now. He needs no prednisone and no albuterol treatments.

In the state of North Carolina, for those earning at or below the 50 percent area median income, there are only sixty-six affordable and available homes per one hundred renters.[35] Many of the "affordable" homes are not suitable. They are roach and mold infested. The plumbing is inadequate. The flooring is unsteady and there are safety hazards.

In the case of Dante's family, rent burden not only impacted their living conditions but also their savings. According to the Pew Charitable Trusts, rent-burdened households have less than ten dollars in savings.[36] In order to move to the double-wide, Dante's mother cut back on what many consider to be essentials such as clothing and nutritious foods. They cut back on doctor's appointments. Dante had to suffer wheezing and shortness of breath in order for the family to save. What a shame.

I like Matthew Desmond's book on poverty because of its unadulterated truth. He lived with the poor and watched as they allocated each vital penny. A mother found change for french fries for her son with hunger pains. A disabled veteran paid $550 dollars in rent, leaving less than $80 per month to cover all other expenses. An evicted woman had to pay to have access to her items, which were forcibly put in storage following eviction. I was compelled by these stories. I have seen them manifested in my patients that live in poverty. It has opened my eyes to the stressors that impact their lives and ultimately their health care.

Epilogue

As I reflect on this book, I can't escape the fact that I started writing without the reader in mind. I simply wanted to record my experiences in the field of health care. I originally wasn't interested in publication. I had downtime, and so I wrote. It was that simple. I found it to be cathartic. There were so many emotions that I wanted to get off of my chest and writing seemed to be the perfect outlet. After I wrote the first chapter about death, I shared it with a close friend of mine. She is a pharmaceutical representative who has had her experiences with the health-care system. She told me the chapter was provocative and that it needed to be published. She asked whether she could share the chapter with a colleague who is an editor. I gave her my permission. Her review galvanized me to continue writing but to consider the perspective of a reader. I have reviewed these pages many times over and I have asked myself what I want the reader to receive. Why would the reader care about my travels through the practice of medicine?

What I would say is that my life has been profoundly affected by my career, and I do hope that this jumps off these pages. If it doesn't, then I have failed. *Aerik's Anatomy* has made me review who it is that I am. It's easy to have morals and standards, but until these are tested, you don't know who you truly are. Medicine has helped reveal my truths and my many faults. I hope *Aerik's Anatomy* has made you evaluate who you truly are. I hope that you have been thoughtful while reading these accounts and considered your own being.

I'm grateful that medicine has taught me that I never had it all together. The way I processed the stress of medical school and residency, and the stress associated with ever present death, was unhealthy. My ambivalence had a profound effect on my well-being and on the relationships with people close to me. I felt a constant uneasiness that was perpetually wrestling with my spirit … and the uneasiness was winning. *Aerik's Anatomy* has made me so grateful that I was able to revitalize this spirit and conquer my doubts.

I hope you too have a full spirit. I hope that you have found meaning in your life. If you haven't, I invite you to the same place I have been. I suggest that you acknowledge the presence of God. You will not be perfect, and you will not have full understanding, but you will have peace.

Acknowledgments

Jesus Christ

References

1 https://india15.wordpress.com/2015/03/05/
kalighat-home-for-the-dying/

2 Kathryn Spink, *Mother Teresa: A Complete Authorized Biography* (New York: HarperCollins, 1997), 55.

3 Centers for Disease Control and Prevention, https://www.cdc.gov/sepsis/datareports/index.html.

4 *Academic Medicine* 92, no. 7 (July 2017): 976–83.

5 *Journal of the American Medical Association* 316, no. 21 (2016):2214–36.

6 Pamela Wible, MD, "NYC doctor suicides linked to bullying?" May 17, 2018, http://www.idealmedicalcare.org/nyc-doctor-suicides-linked-to-bullying/.

7 *Critical Care* 17, no. 2 (April 27, 2013).

8 "Trump, Congress approve largest U.S. research spending increase in a decade,"*American Association for the Advancement of Science*, March 23, 2018, http://www.sciencemag.org/news/2018/03/updated-us-spending-deal-contains-largest-research-spending-increase-decade.

9 Kimberly Leonard, "US healthcare spending rises to $3.5 trillion," *Washington Examiner*, December 6, 2018,

https://www.washingtonexaminer.com/policy/healthcare/us-healthcare-spending-rises-to-3-5-trillion

10 Bradley Sawyer and Cynthia Cox, "How does health spending in the U.S. compare to other countries? *Peterson-Kaiser Health System Tracker*, https://www.healthsystemtracker.org/.

11 *Journal of the American Medical Association* 319, no. 10 (2018):1024–39.

12 Bradley Sawyer and Daniel McDermott, "How does the quality of the U.S. healthcare system compare to other countries?" *Peterson-Kaiser Health System Tracker*, https://www.healthsystemtracker.org/chart-collection/quality-u-s-healthcare-system-compare-countries/.

13 James Cheng, "Mylan's Upgraded EpiPen Torn Apart by Experts," *NBC News*, September 30, 2016, https://www.nbcnews.com/business/consumer/mylan-says-it-upgraded-epipen-2009-so-experts-looked-inside-n652651.

14 Jonathan D. Rockoff, "Mylan Faces Scrutiny Over EpiPen Price Increases," *Wall Street Journal*, August 24, 2016, https://www.wsj.com/articles/mylan-faces-scrutiny-over-epipen-price-increases-1472074823.

15 Charles Duhigg, "Outcry Over EpiPen Prices Hasn't Made Them Lower," *New York Times*, June 4, 2017, https://www.nytimes.com/2017/06/04/business/angry-about-epipen-prices-executive-dont-care-much.html.

16 U.S. Census Bureau.(2019, Dec 27). Quick facts-Salisbury NC. Retrieved from https://www.census.gov/quickfacts/fact/table/salisburycitynorthcarolina/POP060210.

17 DataUSA. (2019). Salisbury, NC. Retrieved from https://datausa.io/profile/geo/salisbury-nc/.

18 Jessica Wapner, "How Prescription Drugs Get Their Prices, Explained," *Newsweek*, March 17, 2017, https://www.newsweek.com/prescription-drug-pricing-569444.

19 "44 health companies make the Fortune 500," *Advisory Board*, June 12, 2017, https://www.advisory.com/daily-briefing/2017/06/12/fortune-500.

20 Ana Swanson, "Big pharmaceutical companies are spending far more on marketing than research," *Washington Post*, February 11, 2015.

21 Song and Han, "Patent cliff and strategic switch: exploring strategic design possibilities in the pharmaceutical industry," *SpringerPlus* 5 (2016): 692.

22 *New York Times*, https://www.nytimes.com/2018/05/17/health/drug-prices-generics-fda.html.

23 Richard Cohen, "Follow the Money: Drug Industry Campaign Contributions," *Tarbell*, November 14, 2017, https://www.tarbell.org/2017/11/follow-the-money-drug-industry-campaign-contributions/.

24 *New England Journal of Medicine* 354 (2006): 2024–33.

25 *New England Journal of Medicine* 365, no. 7 (August 18, 2011): 629–36.

26 Michelle M. Mello, Amitabh Chandra, Atul A. Gawande, and David M. Studdert, "National Costs of the Medical Liability System," *Health Affairs* (Millwood) 29, no. 9 (Sept. 2010): 1569–77.

27 "Detroit Area Doctor Sentenced to 45 Years in Prison for Providing Medically Unnecessary Chemotherapy to Patients," US Department of Justice, July 10, 2015, https://www.justice.gov/opa/pr/detroit-area-doctor-sentenced-45-years-prison-providing-medically-unnecessary-chemotherapy.

28 "Miami-Dade Psychiatrist Sentenced to Prison for His Participation in Various Fraud Schemes," US Department of Justice, July 25, 2016, https://www.justice.gov/usao-sdfl/pr/miami-dade-psychiatrist-sentenced-prison-his-participation-various-fraud-schemes.

29 "Justice Department Recovers Over $3.7 Billion from False Claims Act Cases in Fiscal Year 2017," US Department of Justice, December 21, 2017, https://www.justice.gov/opa/pr/justice-department-recovers-over-37-billion-false-claims-act-cases-fiscal-year-2017.

30 Phil McCausland, "Residents suffer as Mississippi and 13 other states debate Medicaid expansion," *NBC News*, Nov. 4 2019, https://www.nbcnews.com/news/us-news/residents-suffer-mississippi-13-other-states-debate-medicaid-expansion-n1075661.

31 Nicholas Bakalar, "Nearly 20 Million Have Gained Health Insurance Since 2010," *New York Times*, May 22, 2017, https://www.nytimes.com/2017/05/22/health/obamacare-health-insurance-numbers-nchs.html.

32 Jessie Hellman, "Study: ObamaCare premiums could increase 90 percent over three years for some states," *The Hill*, March 8, 2018, https://thehill.com/policy/healthcare/377465-study-obamacare-premiums-could-increase-90-percent-over-three-years-for.

33 Ricardo Alonso-Zaldivar (AP), "'Medicare for All' Would Cost $32.6 Trillion Over 10 Years, Study Says," *Bloomberg*, July 30, 2018, https://www.bloomberg.com/news/articles/2018-07-30/study-medicare-for-all-bill-estimated-at-32-6-trillion.

34 Mary Gillis, "Uninsured struggle to obtain, afford doctor appointments," *Reuters*, April 12, 2018, https://www.reuters.com/article/us-health-insurance/uninsured-struggle-to-obtain-afford-doctor-appointments-idUSKBN1HJ2V0.

35 National Low Income Housing Coalition, https://reports.nlihc.org/gap/2016/nc.

36 "American Families Face a Growing Rent Burden," *The Pew Charitable Trusts*, April 2018, https://www.pewtrusts.org/-/media/assets/2018/04/rent-burden_report_v2.pdf.

Made in the USA
San Bernardino, CA
12 February 2020